The
Eating Disorder
Solution

Barbara Cole

Note for Librarians: A cataloguing record for this book is available from Library and Archives Canada at www.collectionscanada.ca/amicus/index-e.html

ISBN 1-4120-7593-9

Printed in Victoria, BC, Canada. Printed on paper with minimum 30% recycled fibre. Trafford's print shop runs on "green energy" from solar, wind and other environmentally-friendly power sources.

PUBLISHING™

Offices in Canada, USA, Ireland and UK

This book was published *on-demand* in cooperation with Trafford Publishing. On-demand publishing is a unique process and service of making a book available for retail sale to the public taking advantage of on-demand manufacturing and Internet marketing. On-demand publishing includes promotions, retail sales, manufacturing, order fulfilment, accounting and collecting royalties on behalf of the author.

Book sales for North America and international:

Trafford Publishing, 6E–2333 Government St.,

Victoria, BC V8T 4P4 CANADA

phone 250 383 6864 (toll-free 1 888 232 4444)

fax 250 383 6804; email to orders@trafford.com

Book sales in Europe:

Trafford Publishing (UK) Limited, 9 Park End Street, 2nd Floor

Oxford, UK OXI IHH UNITED KINGDOM

phone 44 (0)1865 722 113 (local rate 0845 230 9601)

facsimile 44 (0)1865 722 868; info.uk@trafford.com

Order online at:

trafford.com/05-2488

10 9 8 7 6 5 4 3 2

Table Of Contents

Acknowledgements

IT TOOK MANY GREAT PEOPLE to transform this book from a long-held dream of possibilities into a useful reality.

Drs. Paul Watzlawick and Richard Fisch of the Mental Research Institute in Palo Alto, California, developed many of the strategic and systemic theoretical and practical concepts utilized in the No-Resistance Treatment of Eating Disorders. This new method is slowly gaining acceptance and is being applied by clinicians and interventionists on an international basis in hospitals, residential treatment facilities and in private practices. It originated from the eating disorder program at the Victorian House of Newport Beach, California, and is utilized and referred to in layman's terms throughout this book.

Peggy Claude-Pierre of Canada developed a revolutionary and effective set of concepts with which to understand and treat eating disorders, and world-wide clinical acceptance and applause for this magnificent healing work is still growing. Enough has still not been said about the positive effect of this remarkable woman's contribution to the field of eating disorder treatment and understanding.

Betty Ford Center in Rancho Mirage, California, had the great foresight and good judgment to place me in any proximity to their then Clinical Director and later, Director of Psychological Services, Dr. Nancy Waite-O'Brien, who was a terrific mentor, a good friend and the finest example of excellent clinical skill, professionalism and judgment one could ever hope to emulate. The support that she and Terry O'Brien sent my way long ago furthered my interest in changing things for the better through publication. Their help with the publication of The Gifts of Sobriety (Hazelden Publishing and Information) will always be remembered with extreme appreciation. The Betty Ford Center itself provided me with many important opportunities to grow as a professional in the chemical dependency and eating disorder fields, and I am grateful beyond words for the score of patients who are now leading healthy lives as a result of allowing me to make a therapeutic contribution to their efforts during the time that I worked there.

My association with Bill Swiney and Carl and Barbara Mosen of Sober Living By the Sea in Newport Beach, California, as well as the many administrative and counseling staff who bring the daily miracle of recovery from drug and alcohol dependence to thousands, has been one of the finest surprises and gifts of my professional life so far. Visionary people who turn dreams into realities are how I think of these bright, soulful and enterprising people. Their trust, support and confidence in me as well as the brilliant advice and direction from Bill Swiney as Executive Director over the Victorian House program as well as all of the Sober Living by the Sea programs brightens and enriches my spirit each and every day. Carl, Barbara and Bill, along with Bruce and Sandy Levinson, Elizabeth Robertson, Dr. Kevin McCauley (and many important people at Sober Living By The Sea who are so supportive yet too numerous to mention here) are the ultimate catalysts of service work, and I admire them and feel something beyond a deep sense of gratitude...it is good to truly love the people that I work with.

Dr. Ralph Carson, Dr. Carolyn Ross, Dick Wilson, the board and members of the International Association of Eating Disorder Professionals, Sierra Tucson Treatment Center, Rosewood Treatment Center, Dr. Jerry Brown, and so many other eating disorder professionals and programs are all a major part in positive efforts toward achieving synthesis within the eating disorder treatment provider community. Their support and continued excellent efforts within our field are greatly appreciated.

There have been texts, both historical and practical, that relate to the positive experience of providing effective treatment and intervention related to eating disorders. Where any text has stood out as especially helpful or contributory to the No-Resistance Method of Eating Disorder Treatment, I have credited and referenced these at the end of this book in the bibliography. Each is well worth reading, especially where financial resources are too restrictive for families to afford good, prolonged formal inpatient treatment. There is still much hope for healing in any family that is willing to do the reading and research, and finally take action upon what they learn from these texts. My hope is that this one, in combination with so many others, will serve as a general, informational guide toward providing relief to those who suffer from this disorder as well as for those who care for them. *The Eating Disorder Solution* is not in any way meant to be used as a substitute for inpatient, residential or other effective forms of treatment. Those who suffer from active eating disorders should always consult their medical doctors for advice and assistance.

It is fine and well to have a useful theory, but then, it remains only a theory, untested, untried until one has the opportunity to utilize one's theory with real, live patients. It is clear that the real-time success, year after year, of my No-Resistance Treatment method while Clinical Director at the Victorian House programs in Newport Beach is entirely dependent upon an incredible staff, who interprets and acts upon the theories and strategies proposed with increasing finesse over time.

I want to give special thanks to my mother, Dee Cache, who is a creative thinker and writer in her own right, and an enthusiastic supporter of my altruistic and professional goals. A writer and psychotherapist cannot hope for a better parent than the one that I was given. My dear and departed grandparents, Eve and Bill Edelstein, I know, would give me those precious looks of approval I long enjoyed while they were living, if they were here to read my books, peek into my clinic and private practice and see what all their love and support has been used for when put to the service of others. My aunt, Lynda Palevsky, has been a critically important angel here and there throughout my life. Our paths seem to cross exactly at the time that I need to know something important. Best friend, Susan Cruz, gets the lion's share of appreciation and real-time gratitude for she has been with me through the process of many writing projects. Her steady support and understanding have been my greatest treasure.

For those that space restrictions will not allow me to mention, thank you for listening and believing in me. You are in my thoughts daily with

---

so much appreciation. You know who you are. To my many current and former patients, thank you so much for deciding to do your healing work in my presence. My gratitude to you is endless.

And, for you, the reader, who is either someone attempting to create a healing effect on an individual or a family suffering from an eating disorder, or someone just as fascinated as I have been at the confounding, paradoxical nature of this disorder, I take my hat off...to your open mind, to your desire to increase your own health and happiness as you work with one of the best populations of patients available: those suffering with eating disorders and those who care about someone who actually has this disorder. May you literally enjoy both the learning and practice, as well as all of the good outcomes that result from the setting aside of what you already know, taking in of new ideas and willingness to practice your new knowledge differently than ever before. I acknowledge you for your courage, curiosity and fortitude. I wish those who are still suffering from this disorder exactly the same thing: May you all enjoy the blessings of great health and happiness, freedom from the limitations posed by eating disorders and delight each day in the beauty of this life that God has made possible for all of us.

Dr. Barbara Cole, MFT
Newport Beach, California

.

Forward

Forward By Carolyn Coker Ross, MD., MPH, Chief of Eating Disorders Program and Head of Integrative Therapies Dept., Sierra Tucson Treatment Center, Tucson, Arizona:

Barbara Cole's book, *The Eating Disorder Solution*, is a remarkable contribution to the understanding of the underlying mechanism of eating disorders. The book allows readers into the inner sanctum of the thought processes gone terribly awry in the victims of anorexia, bulimia and compulsive overeating. Dr. Cole's deep understanding and compassion for eating disorder victims is clear and evident. By shining a light on the dark and powerful thoughts that slowly but surely exclude, condemn or frighten away loving family and friends, Dr. Cole has broken the secrecy upon which these thoughts feed.

As she says in her book, "we cannot fight what we don't understand." *The Eating Disorder Solution* offers a road map with which victims suffering from eating disorders and those who care about them can navigate the terrain of what she calls the "unhealthy thought territory" – a concept that serves to give a voice to the separate nature of the eating disorder. The book then outlines an effective strategy for regaining control of the healthy thought territory that has been subsumed by the negative thinking that is part and parcel of this disease.

The Eating Disorder Solution goes beyond teasing out an understanding and definition of eating disorders to offer an "insider's view" of how the disease changes thought processes, eats away at self confidence, and overtakes its victims. It debunks the myth that parents are to blame for an eating disorder and returns them to their rightful place as an ally to their loved one who is its victim. This book also will enable the reader to feel empowered in the face of such an adversary by providing specific tools that can be used to identify the eating disorder even at its earliest stages, to determine how far the eating disorder has progressed and perhaps most importantly, to track the process of recovery.

There are many books on the market about eating disorders and many have benefit to patients and their families. *The Eating Disorder Solution* is one of the few that presents a unified approach with a pragmatic and proven solution. It is a book that can be read by therapists and doctors, patients and their families or by anyone who wonders "What can I do to help?" In the face of the difficulty in treating and maintaining recovery from this difficult spectrum of diseases, the clarity and thoughtfulness of *The Eating Disorder Solution* offers a comprehensive and effective approach that has been proven to work.

Forward by Ralph E. Carson, RD., Ph.D., Board Member, International Association of Eating Disorder Professionals, Consultant to the Women's Center: A Pine Grove Program, Chief Science Officer of Monarch Health Services:

Given that eating disorders manifest as invisible self-destructive thoughts prior to puberty, the question of how to recognize and intervene is one of the most compelling questions asked by family and friends. *The Eating Disorder Solution* is a concise, reader friendly and authoritative book that not only educates, but also provides a solution based approach to these and other questions related to this life-threatening disease. Dr. Cole's method is an exciting and creative approach to assisting the eating disorder patient to reclaim their true self. The methodology presents a balanced and unified approach that recognizes the need to meet the patient where they are at and avoid the creation of confusion. The text introduces a workable plan to achieve complete remission by understanding the cause, connecting with the patient, and calculating success. The message and concepts are clearly communicated, but one will want to read it a second and third time and share it with others. I recommend this book to any therapists or treatment programs' library that has ever sought ways to confront the resistant patient, break through denial and move onto recovery.

Introduction

SINCE THE LATE 1800'S, MEDICAL, psychological and psychiatric practitioners have wrestled with the confounding, paradoxical and elusive nature of the problem of eating disorders. Once a diagnostic category and label was officially adopted, many have wrestled with the problem with limited success. Today, eating disorders are prevalent and growing within people throughout many countries around the globe. As of this writing, there is no well-known 'cure' for eating disorders, and people continue to suffer and die needlessly. This is one of the most difficult disorders to treat that also has one of the highest mortality rates, and continues to confound even the brightest and best among our ranks. All of the above negative statements raised in me a war cry of sorts. I did not want to take on just any problem, I wanted to make my contribution to a problem that eventually would have a solution, and I believe that in this lifetime the problem of eating disorders will have an absolute solution.

I do not profess to be one of the brightest or even one of the best among us, however, I have had the life long goal of making a significant contribution to humanity and on the strength and drive of my conviction toward this end, have selected the problem of understanding the dynamic of the malnourished mind from a psychological and spiritual viewpoint as my raison d'etre. I maintain that one cannot create an antidote unless one understands the complete properties of the poison. Understanding the psychodynamic of eating disorders is the best contribution that I, as one contributing unit of life energy, can offer. Understanding more closely the dynamic in a simplistic way offers understanding to those who have other work to do than study psychology, but still need the information.

The problem of eating disorders crosses many disciplines: physiological, genetic, medical/neurological, psychological, nutritional, psychiatric and spiritual. Seen as a merely physical manifestation, eating disorders persist. Seen as merely a psychiatric or neurological phenomenon, eating disorders persist. The genetic work to cure eating disorders currently being done is brilliant, but cannot undo the sociological/generational damage once a human life has been created. No single discipline can succeed in an attack and coup against eating disorders. Multi-disciplinary approaches are now being used with fair to good results world-wide, however, despite this moderate if sporadic success, eating disorders continue to grow and persist all over this world.

This book is not intended to be a cure for eating disorders. It is to focus all of our minds on a solution. I believe that the antidote to the poison of an eating disorder is to understand the poison, or the eating disorder itself. In working from so many angles with patients, I have repeatedly noted that the dynamic of the malnourished mind is concrete, traceable, repeatable from one patient to the next and, thank heavens, *knowable*. Patients caught in the trap of the eating disorder thought process think and behave like all other patients caught in the same trap. As varied as the human personality is from one person to another, an eating disorder practically erases the individuality found within each personality and replaces this precious individuality with its own cookie-cutter version of an eating disordered personality.

In this regard, one can think creatively about eating disorders as a form of 'possession', and if one were a science fiction fan, one could easily translate the dirty work of an eating disorder to some kind of "pod" that drops into one's consciousness from outer space and turns whole communities into transformed, robotic self-destroyers.

Utilizing a creative and simplistic method to turn over understanding of the psychodynamic of eating disorders to the general public, then, is my ultimate contribution to the eating disorder solution. When everyday people understand this everyday disorder, part of the means of the disorder to destroy people has been abolished.

Eating disorders, in part, do their destruction by setting up shop within the 'doctor/patient' dynamic. Anyone attempting to wrest an eating disorder from someone suffering from one is identified by the mindset as an object of ultimate resistance. Therefore, handing the means to heal directly to patients and their families bypasses this insidious road block to healing from eating disorders.

Part of the so-called 'poison' of the eating disorder contains its own solution. The person suffering with the disorder is the only one who can effect their own healing. People outside of the one who suffers can only become allies of the part within the patient which wants to be well. Any other stance merely feeds and grows the eating disorder until it, using the energy of treatment providers, kills its patient.

When a patient lends their blind faith (since an eating disorder ruins a person's sense of trust at its mid-stage) to a doctor or therapist, it is up to the healing professional to understand the proper stance to take when working with someone afflicted with an eating disorder.

All too many times, the omnipotent stance has only served to become usurped energy by the eating disorder within the patient. With an eating disorder, too gentle and compassionate of a stance also nets the same result. The stronger the intellect, the more creative the mind of a once-healthy person, the greater the cunning resistance of the mindset of the resident eating disorder within the person. The mind is turned in a cancerous way against itself, and all outside stimuli is used energetically to destroy its victim.

While the above description is hideous and depressing, the poison is not difficult to deconstruct and understand. A mind that can grasp simple understanding about what is gripping it, limiting it and killing it over time is a mind that can fight back for its own health. Turning a person's mind against itself, then, is part of the solution to healing from an eating disorder.

This book by itself is not a solution, but the creative method of understanding the dynamic of the eating disorder is in and of itself one of the strongest supports toward creating a solution. When treatment providers and families alike have the same understanding of just what this confounding and paradoxical disorder is, it is my belief that they will inherently know what to do with the information. I hope that by describing, in novel, lay terms, how an eating disorder thought process works, The Eating Disorder Solution will suggest to anyone concerned what needs to be done to conquer eating disorders once and for all.

Ultimately, the nature of an eating disorder is not difficult to understand. As long as the brain is still active, an eating disorder can be turned around and conquered. For as many who have suffered from this disorder, there are a significant number who have healed. Many texts describing their healing process repeatedly reveal a definite pattern to this process. My contribution is an amalgamation of the best of many of these.

Using the adage, "fight fire with fire", this book suggests that what makes up an eating disorder thought process is the same stuff with which one fights back with. Eating disorders, for example, exist in a framework of increasingly concrete thinking. It is concrete thinking that is then understood, properly interpreted by a victim or sufferer and utilized when one wishes to become well.

As soon as family, friends and treatment providers stop speaking their own language of "healthy normal common sense" and begin to speak the concrete, numerically based, incremental and achievement oriented language of the eating disorder, I believe that a solution to the problem of eating disorders will finally be reached.

For now, I only ask for an open mind as you consider the possibility of using this text as your own map and flashlight to guide someone you love back up through the varied levels of hell that exist within their own mind. Those who have interpreted their own way to utilize the concepts mentioned in this book have effected and enjoyed a great deal of freedom from the grip of an eating disorder. There is no better definition of a solution than that.

Chapter 1

NO MATTER WHAT YOU HAVE already read, studied or heard, an eating disorder at its core is a thought process. An eating disorder does not exist first in the physical body, it exists first and only in one's thoughts. What one thinks, one often takes action on. When one has an eating disorder (hereafter called "e/d"), the thoughts containing specific ideas and instructions pertaining to the e/d become too strong to resist by the healthier side of one's thoughts, (hereafter called the "True Self" or "t/s") and at some point, these e/d thoughts must be acted upon.

When a person with e/d acts upon the strong thoughts that have overlaid or encroached upon the true self thoughts, the physical body begins to manifest these thoughts in the form of actions. E/d actions, once discovered, can be alarming, frightening and concerning for everybody involved, including the person who is suffering with the e/d. No doubt you have noticed enough of the outward actions or symptoms of an e/d in yourself or someone you care about, for that is why you chose to read this book. You want to end the suffering, worry, anxiety and threat of loss of yourself or someone you love.

There is a solution to the problem of eating disorders, and it is completely dependent upon your first becoming educated as to what an eating disorder *really* is. As you continue reading, you will learn not only what an eating disorder is, but beyond that, you will learn what the process of recovery looks like as well as the appropriate timing and content of a good aftercare program which will disable the e/d from returning.

Misunderstanding, simple 'not-knowing', confusion and disparity between professionals treating eating disorders and defensiveness by all involved combine to keep an eating disorder stuck in the "problem" mode. Understanding, education, simplicity of method, cohesion and openness are exactly what is needed to begin an effective healing process. This is called The Eating Disorder Solution.

If there is anything positive to say about eating disorders, it is that among all of the diseases that one may unfortunately encounter along the path of one's life, an eating disorder is absolutely traceable, trackable and knowable. For centuries, eating disorders have confounded the medical, religious, psychiatric and psychological disciplines. Each discipline through the ages has attempted to describe and treat eating disorders only to be confounded by the resistance to healing found in an e/d patient, as well as resistance so often found in the families of someone afflicted with an e/d.

Despite the puzzlement and poor treatment outcomes, e/d patients and families continue to attempt to heal from this disease and often their very efforts to do so are met with increasing frustration, confusion and anxiousness. These feelings often result in a sense of futility, hopelessness and all too many times, tragic loss of a loved one.

The statistics related to the high level of fatality due to eating disorders are quite grim, and the numbers of those who relapse or return to an eating disordered state after one or more serious attempts at treatment are just as alarming.

Practitioners in the field of eating disorder treatment are often constrained from providing the highest quality of care by financial constraints, simple ignorance in the greater field of care-givers, misunderstanding by the general public and conflicting information and influence from the general print and visual media. All of this and more contributes to a sense of panic or anxiety in families who have someone within their midst who suffers from an eating disorder. However, this does not have to be the case.

Although it is a very unusual idea, it needs to be stated here that eating disorders in and of themselves are actually relatively simple to understand, and within such a simple means of understanding, become much more easily and properly treated.

The simple understanding begins when we think that an eating disorder is a type of thought process that repeats itself over and over again no matter who its victim is. A growing number of professionals are noting the similarities between methods that work and methods that do not work, and this is slowly but surely creating a synthesis or 'coming together' in the field of treating eating disorders which is helping to set aside the confusion that has long kept eating disorders active through the ages. We still have far to go in terms of gaining final agreement with regard to proper treatment of e/d among professionals in many disciplines, but this is a long term process as much as we wish it to be otherwise. In the meantime, there is much that you can do to promote healing in yourself and your family as it pertains to an eating disorder, and that information is contained in this book.

Understanding the thought process of an eating disorder is the key to succeeding in breaking its strength. It is true with so many things, including unlocking the code to an eating disorder, that often the answer is too simple so that in using complex methods, a solution can not be found. But the code to unlock understanding of what an eating disorder really is is just that: elegantly simple. Simple enough to confound very intelligent minds. Simple enough to escape detection. Finally, however, there is a way to understand the thought process that creates an eating disorder. This way involves fighting fire with fire, utilizing a single form of decoding the thought process, and a simple method involving unity among all persons involved to create healing.

An eating disorder can be simply understood as a separate set of negative thoughts that encroach and grow through time over the total original territory of a person's healthy thoughts. Understanding the idea of 'thought territory' is a fundamental concept contributing to putting an e/d in permanent remission. We will use the idea of 'thought territory' to understand the separate nature of an eating disorder. After all, we cannot fight to get back territory we originally owned unless we are well versed as to the nature of the enemy who has taken it from us.

The solution to putting an eating disorder in permanent remission involves fighting a war to regain original, healthy thought territory (referred to as the 'True Self'). In fighting any war, whether it is on a battlefield of land or on a battlefield of symbolic 'thought land'; we will need to do advance intelligence on our enemy, the eating disorder.

Like any enemy, the e/d has usurped the best supplies, brainwashed the population of people around the territory and stolen away for its own employment our best allies. Those that can be utilized as allies of the true self are some of the first targets to be conquered by the eating disorder. Given this scenario, it doesn't take much brain power to figure out that in a war for territory, the most effective strategy for a coup or takeover would be to kidnap and brainwash the king and queen of our symbolic 'country' or territory of healthy thoughts. Here, the king and queen are commonly the mother and father or primary caregivers of someone who has been plagued with an encroaching eating disorder. Parents of children with eating disorders need to be returned to their rightful place as allies of the True Self living within their children, as was their intention in all of their actions from the start of life itself.

There isn't a single parent of a child who has developed an eating disorder who would have wished such a barbaric and hideous enemy upon their children. Almost all parents of those with eating disorders are given toward the same traits which exist in their children. In a word, a family plagued by an eating disorder is usually an excellent family.

In a following chapter, we will go over where an eating disorder comes from, and surely in understanding this new way to view the origination point of eating disorder thoughts, all readers will be relieved by the good news. For now, in understanding what an eating disorder really is, we need to stay focused on some specific points.

First, to fight an eating disorder, each member of a family must decide whether they will commit to being either an ally or an enemy of the eating disorder. It is almost certain that nobody will be so foolish as to wish to be an ally of an eating disorder, but in becoming educated about what an e/d really is, each family member and friend or professional involved in the process toward a solution (or putting an e/d in permanent remission) will have to be thoroughly committed in their given role as a real ally of the True Self that still lives in someone plagued with an eating disorder.

In order to be a real ally of the True Self, sides will need to be taken in this war for the total territory of the healthy thought process.

Those who wish to follow their own method of fighting, separate from the team approach of being of one mind and one single strategy, may say that they are the ally of the True Self, but in effect anybody who holds themselves as separate from the team will actually be utilized by the e/d toward its own dark goal of usurping more thought territory and finally be a part in the demise of the person actually suffering from the effects of losing the war against the e/d.

So the very first and most important point that must be made and agreed to by any family, friend or professional is that, at least for the purposes of conquering territory taken over the thoughts of the one who is suffering, all will behave 'as-if' they are cohesively believing one method, following one proscribed road map or set of directions and will do so despite any internal hesitations or reservations.

Without complete agreement on this first and most important point, there will never be a solution or permanent state of remission wherever eating disorder thinking is involved. This is because the nature of an e/d is such that it utilizes the very best and strongest efforts of those in its environment to conquer its subject, also known as the person suffering from an eating disorder.

To fight fire with fire, the best and strongest in any team, whether parents, siblings, friends, employers or professionals, must be allied with the True Self and all must work together to stay within one single understanding of what an eating disorder really is.

Confusion is the vehicle by which the e/d thought process can most easily conquer more territory. The reason a team needs to be cohesive in its treatment philosophy and definition of what an eating disorder really is is because any confusion about this within the team structure will be utilized by the e/d itself.

By the time that you are seeking help to conquer an e/d, it has usually taken so much territory as to have made itself somehow physically obvious. This means that the True Self within the one suffering from an e/d has been made very weak and therefore cannot fight back all by it/themselves.

The second point relates to the weakness of the state of the True Self once the symptoms of a conquered True Self territory have become apparent enough to alarm the team, or the group of concerned individuals surrounding someone with an eating disorder.

In Illustration No. 1, we see a box which represents 100% of the True Self territory at the time of birth. In Illustration No. 2, we see how at about the age of between 4 to 6 years old, the e/d thought process has begun taking over True Self territory, or thought territory. At this stage, the e/d is not very strong. There are few, if any, physical symptoms that indicate that disordered eating really exists. The person who is about to have a physical challenge for True Self territory later in life, usually around the onset of puberty, may be showing small signs of this initial encroachment such as nervousness in nature, anxiousness, stronger need for habit or structure, reverting to earlier emotional developmental stages (for example, responding to small traumas by returning to bed wetting, carrying a comforting blanket or clinging more frequently to a primary care-giver or parent).

With the initial 10% to 20% of eating disordered thought territory being overtaken, parents are usually not alarmed, but slightly concerned about the finicky eating or other developing habits of their young person, but seldom feel a need to seek professional assistance for them, often mistakenly concluding (sometimes because of wishful thinking) that their child will "grow out of it".

In Illustration No. 3, it is becoming apparent that not only the age of the person is advancing, but also the strength of the eating disorder thought process is growing as well. At or near the time of puberty, the strength of the e/d's encroachment over the territory of the True Self or healthy thoughts is nearing or just passing the half-way mark. By this time, the outward physical symptoms may not at all look troubling, because many people who have eating disorder thoughts are attempting to cope with these types of thoughts by striving for excellence.

All along the way, any attempt at excellence in activities, school work, or general social behaviors is being encouraged by relatives, family members, school systems and other strong social influences such as one's religious community. This is a small part of where the confusion about the nature of what an eating disorder really is comes into play.

A child who attempts to excel in sports, show a high degree of positive involvement in one's community and behave as if they are 'the best' escapes any suspicion for the real drama that is unfolding internally. We are accustomed to believing in what we see, and in holding great significance in one's actions as the overall indicator of whom one really is. But here is where the thought process of an eating disorder becomes stronger and more sneaky in its tactics to overcome its victim. The greater the effort of someone with an eating disorder to show how excellent they are, the greater the strength of the underlying eating disorder thoughts actually are.

Let's take a moment here to describe as closely as possible some of the thoughts that someone with an early eating disorder is experiencing but never revealing:

Eating Disordered Thoughts at Approximately 50% Strength

1. I take up too much space in the world
2. Everybody can do this (whatever is being attempted) better than I can do this
3. Everybody thinks I am special and unique but I am anything but special and unique
4. I can't do anything right
5. Nothing I do amounts to anything good
6. Nobody understands me and nobody ever can or will understand me
7. If anybody knew who I really am, they would hate me
8. I hate myself
9. The world would be better off without me
10. I am fat
11. I am ugly
12. Nobody will ever love me just as I am
13. I look funny, unusual, different, weird, worse than others

14. Whatever I attempt, it will never come out right
15. They say they love me but they really secretly do not
16. They love everybody else more than they love me
17. Nothing I do is any good
18. Good things that come from me are freaks of nature, flukes or accidents
19. When I do good things, it is because someone else made it happen, not me
20. The only thing I can do well, whatever it is, is something that someone else can always do better at
21. My parents love me because they have to, not because they naturally do
22. If my friends know me for who I really am, they will no longer want to be my friends
23. The world is fake
24. I am fake
25. My family is fake
26. I am only acceptable when I am acting and speaking like others want me to
27. I am a freak of nature
28. I won't be able to keep up this illusion that I am fine for very long as someone will find out how flawed I really am
29. I am a loser

30. I will never amount to anything in this life

31. I am not handsome (male) or pretty (female)

32. What I need to succeed is never really there, it just looks like it is there

33. I am not whole

34. I feel empty

35. I want to die but wouldn't dare hurt my family

36. My family really doesn't want me around, they just act like they do because they have to

37. When I receive compliments it is because someone is obligated to give that to me, or it is because they want something from me like a behavior or a favor

38. I see what is coming when I grow up and I don't want that, it is disgusting to me

39. The world is scary and difficult and I don't know how to deal with it

40. I don't belong here

41. I should have been born at another time

42. Everything I do, say and think is wrong

43. I am wrong

44. I am a misfit

45. The only time I feel good about myself is when I look like something everybody else wants for themselves (anorexic and bulimic thinking)

46. The only time I feel good about myself is when I don't feel anything (compulsive overeating thinking)

47. I can't do anything right so I won't do anything at all

48. If I could do the right thing or be the right person, all of this would go away

49. Everybody else likes themselves for real, and I only can act as if I like myself but it is not real

50. I'm stuck in this (ugly) body

51. I want to disappear

52. I only get awards and good grades to make my parents happy but no matter how many I get, it is never good enough

53. I am never good enough

54. I am not worthy.

These are the thoughts (and only a few of them!) that the young person who is being overcome by the strength of an eating disorder has. Well-meaning parents who become privy to the few private thoughts that resemble the above list in their pre-adolescent or adolescent child often chalk up such thoughts as being 'youthful', since it isn't uncommon for the parent to have had similar thoughts themselves. Where these thoughts have manifested themselves in actions, the actions as stated above are generally toward excellence. From time to time, a young person who harbors eating disordered thoughts will manifest these thoughts in negative actions on a small scale, such as choosing school mates who also feel a sense of loneliness, separateness from the larger group, classmates who are beginning to act out in negative ways against their family or community.

It is also possible that eating disordered thoughts take the opposite direction, causing the young person to 'give up' and fail to feel worthy enough to connect with others, take good care of themselves, and otherwise need to begin utilizing large amounts of food to medicate the pain of despair that they are experiencing. Whether the outward behavior is compulsive overeating, binging and purging, utilizing exercise, laxatives, metabolic changing substances or restricting food, it is true that an eating disorder originates entirely from the same source, no matter the outward behavior or appearance.

It is also true that if someone who suffers with e/d is not permitted to practice their current method of expressing the eating disordered thoughts in one type of action, they will quickly switch to another type of action. The underlying reasons for this, as well as potential resolutions will be discussed at a later point in this book, but to understand this concept is to unravel just a bit more about what an eating disorder *really* is.

Most commonly, though, eating disordered thoughts too often go undetected at the age of adolescence for the primary reason that *if found out, someone of influence might attempt to interrupt the e/d thoughts*. An eating disorder always seeks to protect its position of strength. Secretkeeping of the eating disordered thoughts and behaviors is part of having an eating disorder.

Another important point in understanding what an eating disorder really is involves the concept of subterfuge. An e/d thought process seeks to keep itself underground for as long as possible. Any attempt to correct such negative thinking begins the process of resistance. We will go more into resistance at another time, since it is primarily responsible for the greatest despair and pain in families and needs to be both understood and resolved. For now, suffice it to say that those who suffer with eating disorders have a lifetime of assisting their eating disordered thoughts in being present and remaining secret.

If an enemy makes its appearance fully known, it is generally just before certain complete defeat. This is why the general age of first treatment for eating disorders is in the very late teens to the mid-twenties in women, and later for men. The physical symptoms are usually covered up, as well as the thought process itself so that it can continue taking over more and more territory from the True Self within its victim.

If you are only now becoming alarmed at weight loss or weight gain, obvious signs of an unhealthy relationship with food, odd food habits combined with drug, alcohol or other substance use, compulsive exercising, laxative use, over the counter or under the counter chemicals which change the metabolism, listlessness, weakness, depression, extreme anxiety, repetitive behaviors that seem pointless and cuts or scratches on the surface of the skin, hair pulling or plucking, scarring from blemish picking, injuries that can only come from self-harm such as head banging, pummeling one's body with one's fists, etc., you are not necessarily seeing a full-blown eating disorder at work. You may unfortunately only be seeing the tip of the iceberg as relates to the full strength of negativity in the thoughts about someone you care about.

At approximately 50% strength, the eating disorder thought process is troubling and disturbing, but has only begun to ruin your child's, friends or other loved one's life.

The good news is that if you understand clearly the points made in this first chapter, you are well on your way to becoming a strong part of the solution. Even better, catching and confronting an eating disorder when it is only at 50% strength makes it easier for both the person suffering and the family and treatment team to ally against the e/d to win back the True Self territory. At 50% strength, an e/d has not usurped all of the strength of its victim yet, and having the victim of an e/d begin to fight back against the e/d on their own is terrific ammunition toward winning this particular war for the mind, soul and body of someone that you love.

In conclusion, the eating disorder solution is to put the eating disordered thought process in a state of permanent remission. This can initially be achieved by understanding the following points:

1. An eating disorder is a fixed, known set of growing negative thoughts about oneself over time

2. An eating disorder begins long before puberty, at about the time one begins understanding that they are a separate, autonomous human being

3. An eating disorder does not reside in one's body, it resides in a part or

portion of one's mind or section of thoughts

4. An eating disorder has a separate personality apart from the natural, given birthright personality of its victim

5. A victim of an eating disorder has no initial sense of control over the negative thoughts and later, no sense of control over healing from an eating disorder

6. An eating disorder often masquerades under the guise of excellence in all things OR, an eating disorder will go to the opposite extreme and masquerade under the guise of complete failure

7. An eating disorder will go to any lengths to protect itself from being found out

8. Family members will often be the last ones to actually 'see' an eating disorder, even when it begins to manifest itself physically in small ways

9. Confusion is the earliest and strongest form of self-protection that an eating disorder has with which to keep itself resident in its victim

10. Parents are the ones most often wrongly blamed for causing an eating disorder but they are most often the

primary allies in the initial return of the strength of the True Self in a former victim

11. Professionals who treat eating disorders are more often than not unwitting allies of the eating disorder as a result of a lack of cohesion in a treatment and family team, and unfortunately may contribute to disparity within the field of treatment itself by asserting loyalty or rigidity surrounding their treatment method

12. The first line of attack against an eating disorder is a) understanding what an eating disorder really is, and b) all parties involved in the healing process agreeing to, at a minimum, act "as-if" they have one singular method of understanding and treatment that they will never waiver from.

100% True Self Territory

Birth to Four or Five Years Old

Illustration No. 1

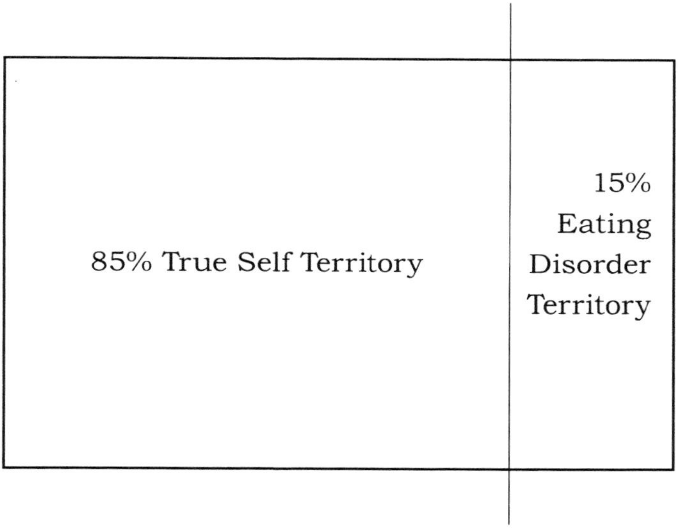

85% True Self Territory

15% Eating Disorder Territory

Four to Six Years Old

Illustration No. 2

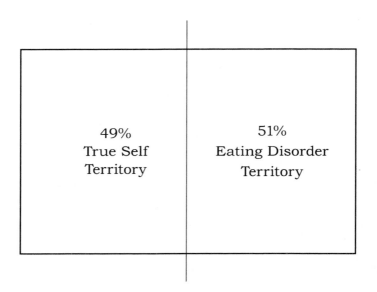

49%
True Self
Territory

51%
Eating Disorder
Territory

Puberty and After

Illustration No. 3

Chapter 2

As was stated in the first chapter, an eating disorder seeks to keep itself hidden while it slowly encroaches over the healthy, positive portion of one's thoughts. It does this so that nobody who may have any influence in a positive, constructive way can intervene or interrupt the destructive process of overtaking the thoughts.

In order to keep itself hidden, the eating disorder thought process masquerades in many forms of behaviors that appear to be above normal or, if sub-normal, at least consistent with a portion of the behavior of others so that it will not stand out. As long as this thought process, as was described in Chapter 1, goes largely unnoticed, it can continue to take over ever greater territory of a person's True Self, or 'truth about one's healthy self'.

There must be a simple, universal way to understand just how much territory has been taken, and the person suffering with the eating disordered thoughts, as well as their family, friends and team of professionals must be able to map out how much True Self territory has been lost and needs to be regained.

In brief, an eating disorder, in order to be properly treated, must first be clearly identified by all concerned parties. Any differences in the philosophy in the method of identification of the eating disorder will contribute to the confusion that was also discussed in the first chapter, and will then be utilized by the eating disorder thought process so that it will gain further territory over the True Self.

While there are many ways to identify and treat an eating disorder, this book proposes only one of many. Whichever and whatever method is utilized, it is strongly suggested that only one method at a time be used, and that all parties involved utilize the same understanding and the same method. This cannot be stressed enough. The enemy, or eating disorder thought process, will intuit any small difference among the ranks of those attempting to interfere with it, and use this difference of opinion to create utter chaos in any perceived group going against the e/d. This chaos typically looks like one caregiver pitted against the other, one story regarding the eating disorder relayed differently to one family member than to another family member, and some friends knowing or attempting to intervene in one way while other friends are attempting to intervene on the illness another way.

This chaos will negate any effective outcome from intervening positively on an e/d at the outset of treatment, thus creating a negative conclusion (i.e., failure) and will, in the meantime, deepen the distress and sense of hopelessness in the family and general treatment team. As this is occurring, the victim of the e/d will receive confirmation that their e/d thoughts are correct in their quiet thought-statements about how worthless and unworthy they are. They will receive outside validation of the same sense of hopelessness and then fail to find strength within themselves and in their general support team with which to fight to regain True Self territory back.

Outside or external negative validation is the method that the eating disorder uses to conquer its otherwise innocent victims. In speaking to one or more people suffering with an e/d, it is not difficult to notice how certain they are of the correctness of their negative thoughts. This is misperceived by those not suffering with an e/d as "stubbornness" or resistance, but in actuality, this misperceived sense of certainty is a large sign of distress and a call for help from a victim of an e/d. Resistance by someone who has an e/d can be translated into True Self language (also known as 'healthy, normal common sense') as a desperate attempt to maintain a sense of sanity.

An eating disorder, via the process of malnourished neurological shifts in perception, slowly but surely changes one's perceptions from what we can term "healthy normal common sense" to its own version of what and how the world is. The two "worlds", one being the e/d world and one being the True Self world, are gradually separated and finally completely split into two paradigms.

This 'split' in perception is why parents and families who have a loved one who is being victimized by an eating disorder are often overcome with frustration and bewilderment. Parents and families are utilizing "healthy normal common sense" to try to understand a thought process that does not resemble the same pattern of perception of the external world as the one being used by the victim of an e/d. A more detailed discussion regarding the critical need for one's external world and internal matching up (also known as "sense of sanity") will follow in a later chapter.

It is clear that you cannot utilize the perception and language of nourishment and receptivity (the commonly held healthy and positive version of an every day thought process) to conquer the perception and language of malnourishment and rejection. In brief, this is a second most common error made by well-meaning families and treatment providers. The paradigm or world view of the eating disorder must be utilized by all involved in the healing process for there to be a strong chance toward actual healing.

This innocent error tragically and all too often turns out to be that the family and treatment provider continually asserts its world view onto a weakened victim of an eating disorder and then expends all of its energy, time and resources repeatedly failing to overcome the eating disorder.

The method of using one cohesive, simple way to fight an eating disorder thought process assumes that *the greater the effort that appears to be required to fight an eating disorder thought process, the greater the misunderstanding as to how to effectively fight the eating disorder thought process may be.* Effective fighting of an eating disorder does not require greater effort, it requires a minimal amount of effort. The thought process involved in having this disorder requires "fighting fire with fire", or matching the right and equal amount of energy with a person's True Self. Going directly against the e/d thought process is a blatant mistake. Clearly, simply and cohesively building a structure of quiet, gentle support around the victim of an eating disorder thought process to ally with his or her True Self is ultimately what can be called *The Eating Disorder Solution.*

Each victim of an encroaching eating disorder still has, as long as they are coherent and living in a viable physical body, just enough True Self remaining to regain their original territory of healthy normal common sense thinking. However, the stronger the e/d becomes, the more territory over the healthy thoughts the e/d takes, the greater the allied and cohesive team force needs to be with the True Self part of the person suffering with the e/d.

The hopeful news here is that no matter how strong the eating disorder has become, no matter how manifest in the physical body it has grown to be, and no matter the physical damage that has already occurred, the positive, receptive mind of the victim of an eating disorder, with the proper approach, can be strengthened.

Time and again throughout the documented history of severe anorexia, bulimia and compulsive overeating, people who have gone to the edge of death have miraculously made it back to what can only be identified as 'normal' living and thinking. And not everybody who suffers with an eating disorder shows signs of having physical damage from the disorder, whether outwardly or inwardly. However, as long as the roots of the e/d mindset or thought process are left resident, no matter how physically healthy on the outside someone may appear, they still carry the thought process of malnourishment called an eating disorder.

If this is not arrested, weakened and kept in remission, this mindset will pass from one person to the next and from one generation to the next, increasing its damage as it grows over time. More information about the origin of an eating disorder will be given in a later chapter. For now, let's turn to the world view, or paradigm of malnourishment, in order to further understand the enemy. Understanding the enemy is to "see" what we are fighting clearly so that whatever effort is expended will be effective and useful rather than ineffective and wasted.

The paradigm of malnourishment as it is manifested in the mind of a victim of an e/d is quite rigid, often referred to as 'concrete'. It experiences nearly everything that comes into its view as black or white, all or nothing, solid instead of fluid, uncompromising, extreme and linear. The eating disorder world view is one of ultimate rejection of anything internally or externally perceived as positive, life-giving or pleasurable.

The alarming numbers of females who come into their womanhood with the mindset of a quickly growing eating disorder is especially horrifying, for just as a young girl is discovering that receptivity is parallel with a relaxed state of being, her own mind is seeking out clever ways to reject each and every positive thing in the world that is literally or symbolically about her womanhood.

While it is proposed that currently over a million males are afflicted with eating disorders, (and this number may easily be far greater than the current research shows) the rejection of incoming pleasure of all types from one's environment is unfortunately more consistent with western views of male behavior and gender identity, causing boys and men with eating disorders to go far longer into the process of destruction from this disorder before it is detected, identified and treated.

In essence, the mindset of someone with an e/d begins as is shown in Illustration No. 1, with nearly all of one's thoughts being positive, flexible, forward thinking, receptive to pleasurable ideas, activities and concepts, and then initially grows into what we can imagine symbolically as a tiny mentally-oriented thought-parasite.

This thought-based parasite grows silently and gradually over time, consuming information about the outside world, and then twisting it into a form that is increasingly more nourishing to its own growth. No doubt you have seen science fiction movies that have similar plots, but the horrifying reality here is that this is not fiction, this is a very real state of gradual thought-possession. The origin of how one initially becomes victimized by an eating disorder will be discussed in a later chapter. The explanation itself contains some of the seeds of healing, not only for the victim of an eating disorder, but for any family member as well.

It is time to return to how the enemy, or in this case, the eating disorder, utilizes the world around it for its own growth over the True Self of its victim. An eating disorder, as has been said, seeks out external proof which then matches the internal negativity felt by someone suffering from an eating disorder. The path of growth of the thought-parasite is initially and originally internal, and this is where the internal negative thoughts described in Chapter 1 first originate.

The thought process of an eating disorder is such that it utilizes changes in actual perception of the world thanks to the neurological state that results from malnourishment. Someone who utilizes bingeing and purging can easily experience a strong change in perception of the outside world thanks to a change that takes place not only in the overall metabolism, but most especially in the way that the brain takes in and processes information about the outside world.

A person who restricts food, uses laxatives or whose e/d utilizes some other more socially acceptable form of disordered eating (such as compulsive exercising or workaholism) is also altering their perception of the outside world. Ultimately, as the malnourished mind takes in information, it is gradually calibrated to shift increasingly to the negative, even though those without an e/d see the world as containing both negative and positive feedback about oneself. A person with an eating disorder increasingly seeks out that which is negative from the whole external environment one is actually in, not because they willfully try to or want to, but because they absolutely must. Their very neurology dictates that this is so.

The longer an e/d has been progressing, the greater its strength, the deeper the malnourishment and the more stunning the negative validation from the outside world will be to the person with the eating disorder.

Parents, siblings and friends of someone with an eating disorder are often puzzled by what appears to be a stubborn refusal of positive validation, as would be the case with simple compliments. Before the e/d becomes too strong, the rejection of a compliment is largely internal, and shows up as a faint but almost audible separate negative 'voice' – not a real voice, suggesting an alarming personality disorder, but the mimicking of one's own voice. This voice sounds legitimate and authentic, and can be 'heard' internally by a person with an e/d as early as age five or six years old.

As the eating disorder gains in strength, encroaching over the True Self 'voice' that can also often be 'heard' internally by young girls and boys, the True Self voice grows ever weaker until it cannot be heard at all. Next in the stage of encroachment over the True Self 'voice' is the exchanging of identity.

In this current age, much is broadcasted in the media about identity theft. We can use concepts from the more commonly understood phrase of 'identity theft' in the media to the type of identity switching or theft that is performed by the e/d thought process to overtake the True Self. With typical identity theft as it is described in the media, a criminal takes a number that corresponds to one's bank account, social security number or other important information and utilizes this single piece of information about oneself to gather more and more information. After enough information is gathered (for example, amount of money in a savings account, home address, telephone number, date of birth), the criminal next uses this collection of information to go directly after valuable resources belonging to the individual *as if the criminal were the individual.*

Similarly, an eating disorder works just like the above-mentioned criminal to use small initial bits of information from one portion of one's thoughts in order to take over use of more and more important personal information. In a later stage, the eating disorder thought process utilizes the information that it has gathered from the internal thought process of the True Self and the external world (parents, teachers, sisters and brothers, etc.) to swap identities so that the person with the growing eating disorder problem cannot tell which part of themselves is "talking" (meaning silently sending messages about the self to the part of the self that needs to take action). Thus, the e/d can be thought of fairly easily as an identity theft criminal.

Once the healing process has begun for those who suffer from this theft of their healthy, normal common sense, the beginning stages of forward movement of regrowth of the True Self involve understanding that the victim of an e/d cannot tell the difference between which part of their thoughts belong to the e/d and which part of their thoughts belong to their T/S. It takes a considerable amount of time for the T/S to become significantly strong enough for a 'split' to develop so that hints of the weakened T/S can be 'heard' in the person's thoughts.

Any exasperation or impatience on the part of the cohesive treatment team to get to the stage where there is a separation between the True Self and the eating disorder can contribute, unfortunately, to a regrowth of the eating disorder over the 'territory' of the True Self.

Impatience, frustration and exasperation are interpreted as outward signs of failure to someone who has lost most of the strength of their True Self. A cohesive treatment team made of professionals, friends and family must be committed to the practice of extreme patience and personal impulse control. The cohesive treatment team must have its own place to vent frustrations and regain strength to fight on behalf of the person suffering with the e/d so that the person suffering does not have to be made aware of these reasonable frustrations. It should be noted that *any external validation for the strength of the e/d over the T/S will cause the cohesive treatment team to help grow the e/d and weaken the T/S..*

The concept of external validation for internal confirmation needs to be carefully discussed in the next chapter since it is so very important to providing a solution to the eating disorder problem. A cohesive treatment team that understands the importance of this concept will be able to regulate how much energy and resources should be expended on behalf of the healthy True Self.

Chapter 3

WHAT THE COHESIVE TREATMENT TEAM consisting of family, friends, co-workers and professionals will want to do in utilizing **The Eating Disorder Solution** is EVICT the eating disorder thought process. EVICT is a acronym which stands for External Validation for Internal Confirmation Technique. EVICTing the eating disorder is a commonly held goal for all team members who wish to ally themselves with the True Self that needs strengthening within someone who suffers from an e/d.

Everyone who is a part of the treatment team needs to understand that if they are emotionally connected to someone suffering with an eating disorder in any way, then they are very important to the healing process. This is because an eating disorder thought process utilizes everything from outside of the person suffering with an eating disorder: people, experiences, comments, television, magazines, newspapers, billboards, facial expressions, body language, one's own reflection, measurement devices (and these are many in type and number)...virtually anything from outside of us, to grow over the total thought territory that once was originally possessed by the True Self.

Remember that the True Self territory was there to begin with, and contains all of the most positive and healthy normal common sense thoughts of someone who has been overcome by an eating disorder.

The eating disorder thought process can be thought of, as was stated in the previous chapter, as a criminal taking over the positive, law-abiding identity of its victim. This type of criminal behaves the same every time, and can be outsmarted by a team of people who understand just how this criminal works. First, it uses everyday experiences and images, reflections and numbers, comments and physical cues, as its method of sneaking into the thought-world of its victim. What may begin as an innocent comment, compliment or criticism of someone who has been targeted for takeover by an eating disorder may end up being used as evidence for external validation for increasingly negative thoughts that exist inside the mind of the victim.

Therefore, family members, friends, teachers, employers, and co-workers who are even somewhat close emotionally to someone with an eating disorder can be utilized by the e/d to hurt the one who suffers. This is because the e/d mindset acts like an identity thief. It does this by using everyday information to create what feels like a 'solid' set of 'facts'. These so-called solid set of facts that are gathered by the e/d thought process are interpreted as what we would term "reality". Of course, the reality about the outside world that is shared commonly with the cohesive treatment team is extremely different than the so-called sense of reality experienced inside the thoughts of someone with an eating disorder.

A victim of an eating disorder grows up gathering information from his or her outside world about him or herself. If books, magazines, television and family members have provided a lot of external information about a victim of an e/d that is even slightly negative in nature, the victim's growing eating disorder mindset can utilize any of this external information for its own purposes. The sole purpose or goal of an e/d is to take over the identity of its victim, and then slowly grow its own type of thoughts over the victim's healthier thoughts, and then become so strong or powerful as to cause the victim to actually believe the negative thoughts about him or herself enough to take negative actions against themselves.

Once this process has become strong enough, it would seem to the cohesive treatment team that there is no stopping the destructive measures a person with an eating disorder will go to show how much self-hatred and self-loathing they really harbor inside. This can challenge any team of well-meaning people, since it is hard to grasp just how mean-spirited these negative internal thoughts are.

It would be easy to underestimate just how hateful and deep these negative internal thoughts go and how far they have spread to encroach and overtake the healthy, positive and normal thinking of someone with an eating disorder. But underestimation of the depth and breadth of hateful thoughts harbored by someone with an eating disorder only helps the criminal disguised as an eating disorder thought process.

This so-called criminal hides by sending messages to its victim that would sound, if the outside members of the cohesive treatment team could hear it, similar to the following statements:

- **You can't lose me**
- **I'm too powerful and you are too weak**
- **You're nothing**

- **I am your best friend and you'll be lost without me**
- **Don't tell anyone I'm in your head/ thoughts or I'll get louder and make you wish you never said anything about me**
- **Keep me a secret**
- **You can deal with me later, maybe, but give me what I want now**
- **Nobody knows about me, see how ignorant they are? So nobody will come to save you from me**
- **Every time you try to distance yourself from me, I will punish you**
- **I am so difficult to figure out that everybody will give up if they even try**
- **It is easy to make me happy, just keep hurting yourself. You don't deserve anything else anyway**

...and so on. If the person who suffers from his or her eating disorder could identify that this thought process was not their own, and if they could speak about the separate messages they hear from their healthier messages, they would probably tell you far worse messages than what you have read in the above example.

So e/d eviction from the mind, over time, is the goal of the cohesive treatment team that must be made up of understanding, patient, compassionate and knowledgeable people who are emotionally connected to someone with an eating disorder. This eviction must occur slowly but surely and gradually over time in order to cause the criminal disguised as an eating disorder thought process or mindset to lose territory over the original, positive and healthy true self. So far, there is no documented proof that eating disorders disappear all by themselves or that they disappear overnight. It must be understood that getting back the healthy thoughts that belong to the True Self happen slowly, gradually and over a long span of time.

Because the identity switching occurs over time and utilizes everyday people who are closely connected to the victim of an e/d, individual therapy is seldom successful in effectively eradicating an eating disorder thought process. Many people who report being helped out of active eating disordered behavior by individual therapy only can still be observed harboring eating disordered thinking which then attaches to other addictive behaviors.

The disappearance of eating disordered actions is no indication that an eating disorder is entirely gone. Instead, when e/d thoughts are present but actions are absent, it means that the e/d simply found another outlet for its hateful messages and will still attach negative behaviors to its thoughts at some point. Some of the more socially acceptable negative actions that stem from negative thinking which is still being fed from one's external environment is alcohol abuse or dependence, promiscuity (in the form of dating or relationships that result in sex and love addiction), relationship issues (in the form of co-dependent and abusive relationships), drug dependence/abuse (in the form of anything prescribed by a medical doctor or anything ingested that is herbal for the purpose of mood alteration, mistaking it for "safe"), workaholism, compulsive exercise, and extreme religious practices (in the form of abstinence from food, water, shelter, one's own resources such as housing, money, physical and mental independence).

The reason that individual therapy has not typically been successful in effectively evicting an eating disorder thought process from the mind of its victim is that the entire external world, but most especially people close to the victim, are utilized as growth material for the eating disorder. Individual therapy generally excludes a constant interactive process with those whom the e/d has been utilizing in order to grow in strength. Therefore, effective intervention should always include those people who have made up the unwitting 'growth material' that the criminal e/d mindset has usurped for its own negative ends.

External Validation for Internal Confirmation technique is what the support system outside of a victim of an e/d must use as part of their

THE EATING DISORDER SOLUTION

total understanding of what an e/d actually is in order to avoid becoming 'used' by the identity switching criminal. Once a member of the cohesive treatment team becomes well aware as to the real nature of the e/d mindset, it is not very difficult to figure out what each person needs to do to avoid becoming part of the encroachment by the e/d.

First, not a single negative or neutral word should be offered for the person with an e/d to experience or hear in any way. While positive words or statements will not immediately heal someone with an e/d, offering any negative or neutral words or statements will actually 'feed' the e/d so that it can grow. It is normal for parents to be corrective, concerned, comparing, or even constructively critical. However, parents of someone with an e/d should entirely leave out such comments, even when they are made as slight innuendo, hints, jokes, etc. A person with an encroaching e/d is highly sensitive and will pick up the slightest negative or neutral comment.

Facial expressions and body language are powerful ways that human beings communicate with one another. No matter how large or small an active eating disorder has become in the physical body of someone who suffers from an e/d, facial expressions and body language that reflect a treatment member's personal opinion about the victim of an e/d should never be expressed. The e/d mindset existing inside someone who suffers not only easily picks up facial expressions and body language, it utilizes this as concrete, factual evidence that every negative feeling and thought they harbor already was an understatement.

Comparisons with other people should be entirely left out by members of a cohesive treatment team, too. The thought process of an eating disorder, as mentioned in an earlier chapter, is very concrete, or black and white, all or nothing. Gradations of seriousness do not exist within the mind of someone whose identity has been stolen by an e/d. Comparing one body to another, one type of behavior to another, one's food intake, metabolism, appearance, clothing, accomplishments, demeanor or personality...all of these need to be left out by those who are joined together to fight an encroaching e/d.

Here is a very important rule of thumb for all cohesive treatment team members to use when dealing with a sneaky, tricky thought process called an eating disorder:

If In Doubt, Leave It Out

Utilizing "If In Doubt, Leave It Out" is an important rule of thumb to follow because it is not so much what one *does* to conquer an eating disorder that is important, it is what one *doesn't* do that is important. Removing material that can be used by the thought process of an eating disorder works very well when people close to an e/d victim are unsure as to what to do or say. This will take some practice. No doubt that by the time you have sought out a book such as this one, you have already tried just the opposite techniques to coerce someone with an eating disorder that they should stop the harmful behaviors that seem so alarming to you. It should now begin to dawn on you that a thought process as sneaky and secret as an eating disorder is would use all of your best arguments, comparisons, facial expressions, attempts at humor, etc., against you. Utilizing *If In Doubt, Leave It Out* confounds the eating disorder for this very reason. At the moment that you might have made a perfectly normal statement with every intention to be helpful or concerned, if you remember this simple rule of thumb, you will be doing quite a bit to remove External Validation from the e/d's ability to change your loved one's Internal Confirmation from positive to negative.

Another method that those close to someone with an eating disorder can do to help EVICT an encroaching eating disorder thought process over the True Self of someone they love is to remove *depth* from being used by the eating disorder as a harmful tool.

Under normal circumstances (in other words, where no eating disorder exists in a person), people often delve into subject matter that is meaningful, or deep, such as how one is feeling at any given time, or bring up subject matter that goes into one's past or future experiences or thoughts.

An encroaching eating disordered thought process will utilize depth as a way to implant a false sense of facts into the mind of someone with an eating disorder. As much as it is pleasant to have a trusting and revealing conversation with someone by bringing up one's history or one's thoughts about the future, bringing up topics that have deeper meaning are nearly always used by the eating disorder mindset to add External Validation to its negative goal of harming its victim.

Therefore, the cohesive treatment team can once again prevail as individuals and as a whole group against the ability of the e/d thought process to conquer its victim by avoiding *depth,* or topics which touch on poignant memories or more in-depth thoughts about current or anticipated events. Removing emotional supplies from the e/d's ability to harm its victim is a powerful way to trick the e/d mindset.

Using EVICT, a good second 'rule of thumb' for a concerned group of family, friends and people who are significantly close to someone with an eating disorder is:

Talk About The Weather

Utilizing "Talk About The Weather" as a second important rule of thumb removes depth as one of the tools that an eating disorder can utilize to harm its victim. Examples of how to use "Talk About The Weather" include keeping conversations up on the surface rather than letting them slowly move into issues that happened in the past.

Staying in the present and only on what is necessary when speaking with someone with an encroaching e/d is important so that the thought process of the e/d cannot utilize depth to create a false sense of absolute negative meaning in someone with a weakened True Self. If a conversation with someone suffering with an e/d begins to move toward the past, or to topics which are volatile or highly emotional, the e/d can be 'tricked' out of using a team member for its own negative means by someone else reminding this person to (jokingly, perhaps) "talk about the weather".

The person hearing the quick reminder of this second rule of thumb should then elect to change the subject quickly to something that is more on the surface of things, like what was read in the today's newspaper, a lighthearted movie, a set of chores for the day, a sporting event, etc.

Remember that it is more often than not what one *doesn't do* than what one *does* that takes away power from the eating disorder to continue overlapping its own negative identity onto the positive, healthy thoughts of someone with an eating disorder.

Chapter 4

IN ORDER TO UNDERSTAND THE eating disorder thought process so that it can be successfully fought and weakened, it is important to understand the psychological forces which are behind this disorder. As has been stated earlier, it is too difficult to fight something that we cannot see, and therefore understanding how control, negativity and perfectionism actually works, where it came from, and what it looks like when a human being is plagued with an overgrowth of it makes it visible and therefore conquerable.

Control is one of the causes as well as one of the symptoms of having an eating disordered thought process. The overgrowth of a negative form of control can leave the victim of an eating disorder with such a limited lifestyle that results in pure misery for themselves and also for those who are connected to them. However, human beings generally require a sense of control over themselves and their world, so while many people may strive to let go of any attempts of control over themselves and their environment, the reality is that control is utilized by human beings to reduce the physiological feeling of anxiety, whether the reasons for needing it are grounded in absolute moment to moment reality or not.

People who have strong eating disordered mindsets generally require a greater sense of control over their entire environment and most especially over their own bodies. There are thousands of texts that have varying explanations as to why this is so, but overall the fact that control is a hallmark of having an eating disorder is not in much dispute in the professional community.

As the thought process of an eating disorder slowly overtakes the thought process belonging to the True Self, the need for control over one's body and environment begins to increase. The progression of an eating disorder is a slowly narrowing trap until there is little movement and a sense of extreme lack of choice when it comes to methods of getting a sense of control over oneself.

This is primarily why when someone is afflicted with an eating disorder, they are often diagnosed with obsessive compulsive disorder. The good news is that, once the eating disorder thought process has been significantly weakened (placed in remission), the need for extreme control over oneself and one's environment is lessened and what used to look like obsessive compulsive disorder now looks like moderate to mild "neatness" and "cleanliness". Certainly there is no diagnostic and pathological criteria for neatness, orderliness and cleanliness when it doesn't impact one's physical, social and emotional life in a negative way.

It can be creatively explained that control comes from a generational history where each generation has practiced a somewhat greater sense of control over themselves than the last generation that came before it. Control can also be creatively explained as actually being a positive human need. After all, not very many generations ago, human beings were much more subject to the forces of nature, and needed to strive for a sense of control over their environment in order feel safe. This safety involved one's ability to regulate heat and cold, as well as stay nourished and housed. There were no emergency numbers, health insurance programs or food banks to access during emergencies several generations ago. Each human being had to have a strong sense over what they would and would not do, in other words, have a great deal of control over themselves and their moment to moment behavior, in order to be inter-dependent on other family members so that all could minimally survive, and maximally, thrive over time.

Taking into account the possibility that control is a positive condition that existed to keep human beings feeling as though they were "okay", it isn't a big leap in our thinking to imagine that each generation, as part of being human, sought to do at least "one better" at important things than the generation that came before it. Any person in an ancient family seeing the results of a greater form of control could see visual evidence of the goodness in it. Control over home living skills, control over one's body, control over one's religious practices, control over the family's work all resulted in a visual and seemingly very real validation that more control would result in more food, better shelter, greater wealth, improved health and more power of choice.

Given this creative explanation, who wouldn't want more control if it promised to deliver all of this in a world fraught with ice ages, barbaric war and cruel political practices, starvation, poverty, cold and famine if one chose not to have control?

And so for hundreds if not thousands of years in a single family history, each generation passed to the next evidence that the more control one had over themselves and their environment, the better their lives would be. It is not surprising to find that in this day and age, the need for a sense of control is extreme in families who have one or more people in them who are suffering from disordered eating. It isn't difficult to imagine that after hundreds of years of improving on techniques and practices to obtain greater and greater control, that getting control over oneself would cross an imaginary "unhealthy" line.

Yet this is exactly what has happened for those who have active eating disorders today. Buried in this very simple and creative explanation about where eating disorders originate is the idea that what once worked very well for your grandparents and parents may never work well for you (if you are the victim of an e/d) because somewhere in a generation just before you or when you came into this life, practices to obtain a sense of control over-reached the boundaries of balance and became extremely unhealthy.

When one is very young, however, unspoken messages passed from grandparents, parents and society at large about how good control is only serve to provide external validation (see previous chapter regarding EVICT) that more control is better. And to push the urge to obtain more control along is our own internal human drive to do whatever our parents did – and do it at least one better than they did.

The concept of negativity works much in the same way that the concept of control does. In this day and age, too much negativity can plague a sufferer with an eating disorder with a series of ever growing thoughts that they are worthless and do not even deserve to be alive. This is the extreme that negativity can grow into once it is framed by the thought process of an e/d.

Magnifying this extreme state of mind for someone with an e/d, the messages from the outside world in the form of television, magazines and other forms of media are messages that the world is not at all a safe or comfortable place to be. External validation for a person's extreme negative thoughts about themselves is so plentiful that it can even convince someone who does not have an eating disorder that the world in general is not a very nice place to be.

When one finds negativity in the world, there are so many other people to validate that negativity that no matter how extreme the negative thoughts are, they seem absolutely real and undisputable.

However, negativity was not always a negative state of thought, but instead was once and long ago a way for human beings to provide themselves with a very practical way to obtain a sense of safety. Once again, using a creative and simplistic explanation that takes into account many generations in the life of a single family, negativity was a way for family systems to impart knowledge about staying safe to one another.

For example, at one time, the earth was thought to be flat. It was believed that if one sailed off into the horizon, one would reach an absolute end to the flat space contained by the earth. If they somehow went beyond that line, monsters were waiting there to consume those that sought to go beyond the confines of the limits of the flatness of the earth. "Don't sail off beyond the horizon line," then, was a statement of negativity. It served to set a limit which would supposedly keep adventurous people from straying too far out of a safety zone.

This is only one of thousands of examples of negative statements used by human beings to set limits about what would provide a sense of safety. People long ago needed to know which areas to stay away from as well as which plants not to harvest and eat. People needed to know which behaviors would result in exile from the safety of the family or of one's country.

If a family learned its lessons about safety very well, it appeared that staying within the confines of the rules of negativity had a positive outcome for all who thought this way. Using the above example related to the human drive to improve from generation to generation on control, the drive to improve on living within a greater sense of safety (or in this case negativity) worked very well the more it was practiced.

Negativity practiced by one's grandparents to their advantage resulted in the passing of this thought process to one's parents. Parents who practiced a great deal of negative thought and the actions that came from it passed this onto their children. In this generation, the process of an eating disorder is reflected in millions of girls and boys who have naturally gone, as their human birthright dictates that they should, to the "one better" state of practicing an extreme state of negativity in their thoughts.

However, as with control, there is only so much negativity that one can harbor in their thoughts and actions before it crosses a very unhealthy line. The statements borne by the e/d thought process are detailed in Chapter 1, What an Eating Disorder Really Is. These statements are creatively and simply described as an amplification of a positive use of negativity from many generations ago.

Let us now turn to perfectionism which can most easily be seen in practice with those who utilize restriction of the intake of food (or anorexia) as their only means of acting upon the eating disorder thought process.

Taking into account the creative, simple multi-generational explanation once again, perfectionism that is now in its extreme form with anorexia can be said to originate from many generations ago where, when practiced in moderation, helped inter-dependent families not only survive, but thrive.

This state of "striving to do better" worked well when it came to practicing the business of trade and farming, and it also worked well when it came to parenting and just about anything else that perfectionism was applied to. To strive to do better and better over time was passed from one generation to the next. Over time, each generation strove to 'do perfectionism' at least "one better" than the generation that had come before it by virtue of our natural drive to improve as human beings.

Therefore, where there is too much perfectionism today as it manifests in young people who inherited this push to do better and better beyond the limits of healthy balance, long ago it was a necessary method of gaining health, wealth and greater choice and safety. It did not begin as a negative state of mind. Perfectionism began as a healthy practice and grew past an invisible line in at least one generation before the person afflicted with an eating disorder mindset could no longer achieve it.

Having a genetic, social, familial and personal drive to strive for perfection but by one's own nature being absolutely unable to achieve it is all the external validation one needs to confirm that internally, one is unworthy of anything good. To get the inside world via one's thought process and the outside world via one's external validation of the inside world synchronized or lined up, a person must begin to reject from their sphere of influence anything good and become very good at seeing only the evidence of (false) facts that one is unworthy and therefore 'bad'.

Anorexia may be the easiest form of eating disorder wherein perfectionism can be seen, but it is not the only form of eating disorder where perfectionism actually exists. Bulimia, or the taking in and expelling of nutrition in unhealthy ways provides a somewhat less obvious but still absolutely consistent method of a person gaining external validation for an internal sense of unworthiness.

Compulsive overeating shares the same exact state of mind with all other forms of eating disorders, even though the physical practice does not involve restriction or expulsion of nutrition so much as it involves taking in of too much nutrition and holding on to it. No matter the visual or external ways that eating disorders are practiced, the mindset is always the same. The person, by virtue of control, negativity and perfectionism, becomes increasingly trapped inside a set of growing negative thoughts, need for absolute control over one's feelings, and practices either extreme perfectionism, and failing their ability to achieve perfection, often removes themselves from ever striving for it in the first place.

Perfectionism that has crossed an unhealthy line can be seen by an informed parent in its early form when a child refuses to participate in a team or competitive activity. Internally the negative thought is already implanted that, "if you can't do it perfectly, if you can't win, you shouldn't even attempt it". Extreme perfectionism shows up early in life with a desire to outwardly appear to be incredibly neat in one's grooming, very meticulous and organized and finicky or picky about what goes on one's body and what goes inside one's body.

Well before more obvious signs begin to show that perfectionism has crossed a multi-generational line in the generation before the birth of one's child, the small symptoms of unhealthy perfectionism are already being practiced. Practices that worked well for one's grandparents and parents, remember, will no longer work well for the child of today. But because in prior generations neatness, attention to detail, striving for excellence in as many areas of one's life as possible proved absolutely to be have a positive outcome, children suffering from the beginning stages of the eating disorder thought process have all the external validation they need to begin the internal conflict of not being 'good enough'. And unfortunately, it comes from well-meaning parents, teachers, coaches, and the general media and societal teachings at large.

It is understood that no single person would ever wish an unhealthy form of perfectionism on someone they love, but in fact, this is inadvertently and innocently what occurs within families who have one or more people within it afflicted with disordered eating in some form.

In becoming educated about control, negativity and perfectionism, it is not difficult to know what the proper actions should now begin to be. When parents find out about the simple concept of generational 'line crossing' from healthy to unhealthy practices and beliefs, out of a desire to help their own children who have become ill with the e/d thought process they are motivated to change. This change immediately shows up in their own expression of themselves toward their young and adult children.

The healthiest thing families can do for someone who is suffering with an eating disorder is to first educate themselves as to the well-meaning history of where control, negativity and perfectionism originated from. They must then together discuss ways in which their own beliefs and practices express an overgrowth of these concepts, change their own personal behaviors in order to avoid coming across as hypocritical, and finally, gently undo the passing from one generation to the next of the message that more control, more negativity and more perfectionism is better.

More is not, in this regard, better. More control, more negativity and more perfectionism are actually extremely unhealthy and have contributed largely to the growth of the e/d mindset. Where it is not practical or healthy for any human being to give up some control, some negativity and some perfectionism, those who are emotionally connected to someone with an eating disorder thought process owe it to themselves and to the one suffering with the active eating disorder to make change first within themselves before expecting their loved one to make change.

Chapter 5

ONE OF THE MORE INTERESTING features of people who develop eating disorders is that at the core of their nature or personality, prior to their True Self being overtaken by the eating disorder, they are usually a great deal more altruistic than others. This personality or character trait involves a basic, strong drive to give of oneself to others for the benefit of others.

However, with an encroaching eating disorder, this beautiful facet of one's character is also overtaken, and a person's altruism is then altered so that the very definition is changed into an unhealthy form. This form, if spoken aloud by the eating disorder would be: "Give of yourself to others as long as it takes something from you or hurts you."

An eating disorder makes its victims feel unworthy, worthless and later even takes away the belief that this person has a right to live and take up space on this earth. It is not surprising that the thought process of malnourishment which we call an eating disorder changes the meaning of all things for the one who suffers with it. It is also against anything that is inherently spiritually satisfying and overall incredibly positive or uplifting to the soul.

One of the last character traits to disappear in the morbid progression of the disorder is one's altruism. This is because altruism is attached to one's original personality or spirit. Only when the spirit is ready to detach from the body (and in the case of eating disorders, only when the disorder has brought its victim to death) can altruism be conquered. That is how strong it is. Often the drive to behave in an altruistic manner is quieted when the eating disorder becomes so active as a set of physical symptoms in the body that the person with the disorder becomes too physically weak and/or ill to perform actions that satisfy their basic altruistic needs.

It is important to recognize any type of altruism in any form in the one who suffers with an eating disorder, because it is altruism that often will still respond to family, friends and treatment providers' efforts to help separate someone from their eating disorder. The desire to care for others at the exclusion of oneself or one's own needs may look like martyrdom on the surface (or hundreds of years ago, religious asceticism), but is actually the overtaking of a pure and beautiful personality trait that belongs to the True Self. The journey to healing is more often than not measurable by one's ability to move from taking from oneself and giving to others to giving to others and nourishing the self.

It is not unusual to find those who have recovered from eating disorders in the helping professions since helping others is such a large part of the original drive toward altruism. Police, hospital workers, physicians, teachers, religious leaders and so many other people who chose helpful work and service to others are easy targets for this disorder. Yet it is the strong desire to help others that can be accessed by family, friends and caregivers to 'hook' into that part of the person suffering with an eating disorder in order to access what little strength is still remaining of that person's True Self.

Altruism in and of itself is the single trait that stays joined with the True Self even when an eating disorder has become very strong. Even when the strength of the e/d is so great that the victim's body is finally in physical decline, the desire to be helpful to others is still accessible. This can easily be seen in situations where patients who can barely stand up or walk due to weakness from loss of muscle mass will push themselves to do so in order to help another patient. Another example of this can be seen when a very weak and ill patient 'puts on a face', or spends what little energy they have in order to make themselves look healthier just in time for a family visit. This is a form of altruism in that a) it covers up the depth of the eating disorder so that its consequences can be hidden and thus perhaps uninterrupted, and b) it spares the feelings of the family, friends or others who wish to visit the patient and lifts their spirits.

This is the form that altruism takes once the e/d has successfully taken it over. It harms the person with the disorder but spares everyone else, or at least prevents the sufferer with the e/d from feeling guilt for allowing their disorder to cause someone close to them any emotional pain.

In my other text, *The No-Resistance Method of Eating Disorder Intervention*, I utilize a great deal of connecting to and appealing to whatever healthy altruism is still accessible in the resistant and very ill person needing treatment. People who will not allow themselves to receive help will often tolerate receiving help as long as it helps other people that they have an emotional connection with. This is a key point for those wishing to help someone with an eating disorder: The internal dynamic of an eating disorder is outward energy, or rejection of nourishment. In the case of soulful or spiritual nourishment, an understanding of this outwardly directed energy is key.

More will be revealed later about how altruism joins with a person's desire to avoid guilt and shame. There is much to learn about how an eating disorder utilizes concrete thinking in the form of data or numbers to further weaken its victim, but it should be noted that it cannot do this without the sufferer's attempt to put a facade of normalcy or goodness on it by utilizing their overtaken and unhealthier version of altruism.

If you have noted that someone suffering with anorexia will expend a great amount of energy cooking and serving food to others but will take no food for themselves, you have experienced first-hand the overtaken form of their altruism. This behavior can also be seen in those suffering from bulimia and compulsive overeating.

As has been stated before, the manifestation of the eating disorder at the physical level is not as important as the internal dynamic of how the eating disorder works. Fortunately for us, the internal dynamic of an eating disorder works in the same way, over and over again, even though it has different outwardly-looking effects on one's body and lifestyle.

In getting to thoroughly know the dynamic of the eating disorder, each person wishing to be of true help to someone who suffers will be able to tailor their thoughts and actions so that they are fully aligned with the resurfacing of the True Self and the effective efforts to submerge and drown the eating disorder.

Chapter 6

THE EATING DISORDER THOUGHT PROCESS is, as it makes progress over time to conquer the True Self, very concrete. The word concrete when used here means that a person's thought process becomes more "all or nothing", or more "black and white" and it also becomes, above and beyond everything else, quite rigid.

This rigidity is often seen as obstinate or more often, stubborn behavior. As the disorder progresses, a person with an eating disorder seems to become more and more stubborn. In fact, the so-called stubbornness seems to grow whenever help is offered. It also appears to become stronger in the face of the eating disorder behavior being 'found out' or discovered by someone who has the perceived ability to intervene on it or get in the way of the progression of the e/d.

Concrete thinking, as it appears to grow and resemble some sort of insane thinking (as opposed to the "healthy normal common sense" thinking of family and friends who do not have eating disordered thinking), can be one of the most frustrating and disheartening features of trying to help someone who has an overgrown eating disorder.

Many who care about the person suffering with the eating disorder remember better days from the past where their own healthy normal common sense thinking still resembled and matched the common sense thinking of the person with a yet to be discovered eating disorder (or an inactive eating disorder).

The frustration begins when the physical symptoms of an active eating disorder are discovered. Sometimes the eating disorder has been active in one's behavior and physical body for a long time, but one or more behaviors tip the scales toward there being a real, potentially life-threatening problem rather than a personality quirk that is being expressed.

The longer the denial that there is a real life-threatening problem, the longer a person suffers with an eating disorder, the stronger the eating disorder becomes. Therefore, if you or someone close to a person with an eating disorder is noticing an increasing degree of "stubbornness" or rigidity together with physical and behavior symptoms that point toward difficulties surrounding food, it is best to intervene sooner than later to try to bring help to this person.

Again, by the time you are noticing a great deal of resistance to common sense suggestions, you can be sure that the greater the resistance, the greater the energy to push away good suggestions and sound advice, the closer to serious physical consequences the person with an eating disorder will most likely be. It is good to have a way to judge how far along an eating disorder has progressed. This is one way that non-professionals can tell, by themselves, when it is time to engage the services of a professional therapist. When physical symptoms are present, always consult a medical doctor first.

Earlier in a separate chapter, the concept of weakening the thought process of an eating disorder by utilizing the phrase, "fight fire with fire" was discussed. Utilizing your own concrete thinking is one way to more effectively counter the thought process of an eating disorder that lives in someone you care about. People who are suffering themselves with an eating disorder can, in fact, "trick" their own e/d mindset using concrete thinking as well. However, as the e/d becomes ever stronger over time, those suffering by themselves will not be able to utilize enough True Self strength to counter the power of the eating disorder and should "trick" their e/d by writing a letter in their own handwriting and leaving it for a parent, therapist or friend to read.

An e/d is not an actual person, place or thing. It cannot be seen. Only its pattern can be seen as it expresses itself utilizing the body of a human being to do so. This is why you are learning, by reading this book, to make the "invisible" "visible". The progression of concrete or rigid thinking can be effectively fought by those who have emotional, financial, employment, legal and other ties or 'leverage' with the sufferer of an eating disorder. As stated above, the person with the e/d cannot themselves begin their own healing once the disorder has become too strong.

By the time you encounter mild resistance to healthy suggestions, the e/d has become too strong for you to wait and see what the sufferer will or will not do. They simply cannot raise enough thought-strength to work around or go over the thought process of the eating disorder. It will always win.

Perhaps one of the biggest mistakes that caring, well-meaning people can make when attempting to help someone with an e/d is to take a "wait and see" attitude. Here is where your intuition or your "gut level feeling" will serve you and the person with an eating disorder very well. Trust your gut. If you think someone has difficulties receiving nutrition, compliments, favors, love, attention, time or money, then what you are thinking is correct: they may already be experiencing an inactive eating disorder.

If you see that someone you care about is rejecting good things and is also showing physical signs of stress, wasting, obesity, bloating, enlarged cheeks, heart problems, weakness or lack of minimal energy, fainting, tooth and gum erosion or yellowing teeth, perpetually cold hands and feet, wearing layer upon layer of loose or baggy clothing, increased use of fabric softener (to name a few physical symptoms of an eating disorder that has now become active), this person needs your immediate and strong help. Understanding the thought process to include concrete thinking will help you work around the person's e/d so that you can more easily avoid so much resistance and rigid thinking and bring help to the person that you love.

Eating disorders exist in a person well before they become physically obvious to others. Because an eating disorder, at its core, is a thought process, it does not first require malnutrition to show up in its earliest phases. People who are in residential or inpatient treatment for very powerful and harmful eating disorders can fairly easily look back after thirty to sixty days of continuous abstinence from the practice of their eating disorder (when healing of the mind has begun) and realize that they had eating disordered thoughts as early as the age of five or six years of age.

Generally, and as stated in most textbooks, eating disorders have an 'onset' at about the age of puberty. However, the word 'onset' is misleading. It is misleading because an eating disorder thought process has two major phases: inactive and active. A person in the inactive phase may appear to have character traits of someone who later develops a full-blown, active eating disorder. The better you are at understanding the eating disorder mindset, the sooner you will be able to intervene and perhaps arrest the encroaching power of the e/d so that it cannot cross over to the active phase.

In the inactive phase, a (typically) young person will show signs of either an extreme need to compete with others or an extreme need to avoid any competition with others. This is because the mindset, if it could speak, sends a firm message to its victim that, where competition is sought, "you have to prove you are worthy".

Where competition is strongly avoided, the eating disorder mindset sends a firm message to its victim that, if it could speak, would sound like "you will never be able to prove that you are worthy so don't even try."

Either competing or avoiding competing shows that the thought process of an eating disorder has already become strong even before it has enough strength to cause a young person to begin to take actions on their own thoughts. Therefore, well before you may see binging, compulsive overeating, heavy exercising, use of laxatives, diuretics, water loading, mood altering substances (over or under the counter), restricting, or other active phase behaviors, you may very well see the beginnings of the eating disorder mindset in just this subtle way.

When pressed to compete when he or she does not wish to, a young person with an inactive eating disorder will expend a tremendous amount of resistant energy to win the argument against competing. The greater the amount of resistance, the more likely it is that there is an eating disorder thought process present and growing. When pressed not to compete, the same great effort toward winning the argument also is revealing in the same way.

Competition shows up in many forms. Concrete thinking means that not only is rigidity in the thoughts present, but it also means that the person suffering with an inactive or active eating disorder requires *evidence* of competing or not competing.

This evidence in young people shows up as needing to win at sports, get better times at a foot race or swim meet, obtain only the highest and best grades and remarks, go above and beyond the regular requirements of scholarship even when fatigue sets in (such as serve on committees, do community service, run for student offices, etc.).

Unfortunately, this colludes with healthy normal common sense of people who do not have active eating disorders but who may have passed a portion of the inactive thought process from one generation to another for good reasons to their young person, such as parents, grandparents, coaches and teachers. Of course we all wish for our youngster to excel and achieve. Of course we enjoy being the parent or friend of someone who is the "best" at dance, sports, debate or track and field. And we want these achievements to cumulatively result in an easier and better lifestyle later on for our young people. However, the sneakiness of the eating disorder mindset is easily hidden from view at these ages because it uses achievement as a cloak under which it can continue to progress and conquer its victim later, when the strength of the e/d causes a person to take behavioral or physical actions directly related to food and related substances.

An eating disorder thought process can be fought with a parent's commitment to avoid allying with the e/d and in allowing a child to just be a child. This means plenty of time for rest and play activities that are not competitive and do not result in an outward reward for excellence above and beyond the general norm.

Many parents of children who have inactive eating disorder mindsets growing within them can be seen driving their children to endless activities such as dance lessons, sports activities, tutoring sessions, extracurricular activities, even though both parent and child are generally exhausted and have no time for unscheduled, peaceful, aimless expenditures of time.

The push to excel in a family of high achievers was once a wonderful thing to collude with, however, with a young person who has inherited an internal push to excel and who is already fairly motivated, further support for 'pushing' only hastens the beginning of the active phase of an eating disorder.

Adults may also show both an inactive and active phase of an eating disordered mindset. Puberty is the general age at which an inactive eating disorder jumps the gap from existing solely in the thoughts to existing both in the thoughts, and in the behaviors.

Often a stressor will serve to increase the external validation that one is not worthy, such as losing a job, losing a loved one through death, divorce or separation, or experiencing a significant traumatic event such as an act of physical, emotional, sexual or verbal violence against the self. Trauma doesn't necessarily cause an eating disorder. However, trauma is often all the external validation for already overgrown internal negative thoughts about oneself that an eating disorder requires in order to jump the gap between the inactive to the active phase.

Remember that what we see with our eyes is not always the way that things actually are. Just because it appears on the visible surface of things that first there was some sort of trauma and next there was an active eating disorder does not at all mean that trauma is the cause of the eating disorder onset. When looking at one or several traumas together with active eating disorders, it is almost always easy to see that first and much earlier in life the eating disorder mindset was present in its inactive phase.

Enough can never be said about concrete thinking as a diagnostic and telling feature of the strength of an inactive or active eating disorder. But more needs to be stated here about how to track the progress of encroachment of an eating disorder over the True Self within a person. Beyond this, we will also need to know how to track the progress of healing where the eating disorder mindset is made weak and the True Self is once again restored to its original or greater than original strength. This topic will be covered in the next chapter.

Chapter 7

AN EATING DISORDER, IF ANYTHING good can be said about it, is traceable, trackable and knowable. This is important to know if someone that you love has an eating disorder, because you will need to know how to fight that eating disorder properly based on one single very important piece of information: How strong has the eating disorder thought process become over the victim's True Self?

It has been stated earlier in this book that you cannot adequately fight something that you cannot see. Because an eating disorder originates in the thoughts, and these thoughts promote maintenance of themselves via a state of secrecy, they cannot usually be seen until they are large enough to cause a person to take action upon the thoughts. As noted in the previous chapter, once someone begins

---

80

to take actions based upon eating disordered thoughts, their eating disorder has become "active". During the active phase, symptoms may begin to show that there is an eating disorder present.

Outward symptoms such as weight gain or loss, eating of foods that feel "safe", avoidance of foods that feel "unsafe", constant weighing of oneself and one's food, etc., do not in and of themselves show the strength of an eating disorder. These symptoms only show that an eating disorder is strong enough to have finally become active. An eating disorder that can be fought during its earlier inactive phase is one that requires less financial and physical effort to conquer. Most people, however, are trained to react to only that which can be seen by our eyes. Therefore, if we have a way to literally 'see' the strength of an eating disorder which is inactive or active, we can launch a better retaliatory attack against it based on viewable information. Viewable information makes more sense to us than invisible, theoretical information.

Remember that creating a solution to the eating disorder problem requires much effort by many people, but that the largest part of the solution is removing the ability of an e/d to confuse and mislead people from the problem of having an eating disorder. One of the most important things you can do then, toward creating a solution to the problem of having an eating disorder is to *make the invisible (eating disorder) visible.*

Let's do this by fighting fire with fire: The eating disorder mindset uses numbers to conquer its victims. Fat grams, calories, weights on a scale, clothing sizes, grades or grade point averages...all of these are examples of numbers that are used by the mind that is overcome with an eating disorder. So let's use numbers back at the eating disorder to expose its size and strength. We will need to adopt some new concepts in order to do this, some of which have been mentioned earlier in this book.

The first concept we will need to adopt in order to see the size of the eating disorder is called **soul territory**. For those who do not believe that a **soul** exists inside the physical body of an individual, the word **personality** can also be used, as in **personality territory**. It is more important to use a phrase such as soul territory than it is to get into an argument about whether or not one has a soul, considering that the argument over these concepts can confuse and distract anyone who wishes to fight against an eating disorder.

Wouldn't the eating disorder love for everyone concerned to get into a disagreement about what is going on rather than for all concerned to join together to take back what the eating disorder is growing on? Well, simply stated, the eating disorder is growing on the soul (or spirit or personality) and its goal is to take all of the soul territory that once belonged to the person and use it for its own fatal ends. The eating disorder mindset or thought process wishes to kill its victim and along the way, make all concerned – family, friends, etc., absolutely as miserable as possible. If it can spread into another generation, it will. The way it can do this is by hiding itself, and promoting arguments about what exactly it is in the first place.

We won't help the eating disorder do this to someone we care about or to ourselves. We will act "as-if" we all call the growth-material of an eating disorder by the same name even if intellectually we all disagree. We will call it "soul territory" so that we can make this invisible concept visible, and then find out how strong it has become.

The next concept we will need to adopt in order to make the invisible eating disorder newly visible is calculation. We need to **calculate**, using certain criteria, how much **soul territory** has been taken by the eating disorder over the True Self. Remember, the True Self is one's birthright, one's natural thought process containing mostly positive statements about who and what one actually is. The True Self sees positive and negative in the outside environment and attempts to turn both positive and negative into positive, productive input for the self.

The eating disorder works in exactly the opposite way. It utilizes a change in the perception of its victim (usually caused by neurological changes due to malnourishment) so that both positive and negative information from the outside environment can mostly be seen as negative information about the nature of one's self.

As the eating disorder grows over time, so does its ability to transform all outside information into inside negativity. As the eating disorder grows, it also gradually removes its victim's ability to tell the difference between what part of themselves are their eating disorder thoughts and what part of their thoughts are their True Self thoughts. The eating disorder thoughts eventually become so much stronger than their True Self thoughts that both sets of thoughts *feel like* they are one set of thoughts instead of two separate types of thoughts.

In order to get an eventual split and separation between these two sets of thoughts (which is part of the process of healing, described in a later chapter), it will be important to know just how strong the eating disorder thoughts are to begin with. We can do this by calculating the strength of the eating disorder.

An eating disorder can be calculated by an individual sufferer or by someone who cares about them by understanding some of the areas that are involved in the takeover process of the eating disorder. Some, but not all of these areas are:

- **time (spent thinking about and acting upon the e/d thoughts)**
- **energy (spent performing e/d actions or hiding e/d actions)**
- **money (spent in relation to food, medications, treatment, etc.)**
- **embarrassment (related to having an e/d)**
- **worry (about an e/d by self or others caused by the e/d)**
- **shame (for having an e/d caused by others and felt by oneself)**
- **social consequences (negative change in social activities due to the e/d)**
- **health or medical consequences (that an e/d has caused)**
- **relationship consequences (discord with significant other due to an e/d)**
- **familial consequences (discord within a family due to an e/d)**
- **legal consequences (example: shoplifting as part of having an e/d)**
- **employment consequences (missed work, tardiness, job loss due to e/d)**

When you or the person you care about who is suffering from an eating disorder thought process takes into account some or all of the above areas where an eating disorder can make a negative impact, a percentage of each of these areas can be applied.

For example, Jane Doe, our imaginary victim of an e/d, has been suffering from inactive eating disorder thoughts since she was about 7 years of age. That is when she first began having strong, negative thoughts about herself. When she was 12 years old, these thoughts became too strong to resist, and bothered her too much. To quiet these thoughts down, she took her first negative actions against herself. By restricting the amount of food she ate, she noticed that the negative thoughts about herself quieted down. If she took in nourishment, she would then increase the amount of exercise she did in that particular day. By the time she was 19 years old, she had learned how to switch between vomiting and using exercise to quiet the eating disorder voice down. She also found that restricting her food helped her to not need to vomit as much since now she was experiencing painful acid reflux and thought it connected to too much vomiting. When she drank alcohol, it also temporarily numbed out the eating disorder negative messages she heard about herself in her own mind. She began drinking more, restricting food more and felt herself becoming less interested in doing anything but these two things. She began feeling too weak to do much exercise. Her family became concerned about an alarming loss of weight. She tried to avoid them but their concerns became stronger even while they told her they admired her for "staying so slim". A knee injury from over-exercising on the treadmill prevented her from exercising so she drank greater amounts of alcohol to keep the e/d voice quieted. This resulted in needing alcohol earlier in the day to stop shaking. She began feeling too much anxiety when any of these behaviors and actions wouldn't work well enough and went to a medical doctor who prescribed an anti-anxiety medication. She became dependent on the medication and the anxiety would often become so bad that she could not attend classes at college. She met a young man who treated her very poorly and this also seemed to quiet the e/d voice. With a loss of friendships, having to drop out of school, being constantly occupied keeping the e/d voice as quiet as possible and keeping the anxiety down, her life was reduced to laying on the couch in her living room. One day her family brought an interventionist to her apartment and helped her face the reality that her life had become unmanageable due to an eating disorder, alcohol and prescription drug addiction.

In treatment, her therapist asked her to state how much soul territory her eating disorder had taken over from who she really was originally, also known as her "True Self". In terms of time, energy, money, worry, consequences to nearly every area of her life, Jane Doe stated that her eating disorder had taken 90% of the territory over her True Self.

In tracking the eating disorder, it is important to give a number in the form of a percentage to the eating disorder in order to see what normally would be invisible. The eating disorder, as a thought process, is unable to be quantified by those who do not have the actual symptoms of the eating disorder. The correct determiner of the number is the person who is suffering from an eating disorder themselves. This is because the sufferer is the one who must do the work to get back their True Self territory. The number assigned to the strength of the eating disorder must "feel right" to the person who must do all of the primary work, even if it doesn't feel right to those who are concerned about them.

Once a number has been assigned to the strength of the eating disorder, both the remaining strength of the True Self as well as the challenge ahead can be more clearly known and understood by the victim as well as those who are there to help him or her. If the True Self, for example, has 10% strength and the eating disorder has gained 90% strength, this makes the journey toward getting back at least 99% True Self quite clear.

The process of recovery from an eating disorder is not an easy or brief one, but it can be done. Tracking the strength of an eating disorder is one of the first primary steps toward conquering it. Next in the process of recovery is tracing progress, and this will be discussed in the next chapter.

Chapter 8

AN EATING DISORDER, AS HAS been stated in an earlier chapter, is trackable, traceable, knowable and curable. It works the same way in different minds of different people. This is fortunate for those who wish to help someone heal from an eating disorder.

If the eating disorder can be thought of as "the enemy", this is indeed an enemy that behaves in a cookie-cutter fashion, functioning the same way over and over again. Its pattern repeats itself in everyone it attacks, and because it operates in this way, it can be tracked (see Chapter 7) as to the amount of damage it has caused and strength over the True Self that it has gained. And because it operates the same way over and over in different people, the process of recovery from an eating disorder can also be traced.

Let's say that the person with an eating disorder has used the method in Chapter 7 to track the strength of his or her eating disorder. They find that their eating disorder mindset has gained 90% strength over their True Self in terms of time, energy, worry, anxiety, consequences, etc. The True Self, it turns out, now has only 10% strength remaining. Rather than think fighting the eating disorder is hopeless because there is so little healthy normal common sense thinking available with which to fight back for True Self territory, a person with an eating disorder can find a sense of hope in realizing just what that 10% is capable of doing.

At 10% True Self, the thoughts of someone with an eating disorder can still rally and fight back. 10% of the positive mind causes someone suffering with the limitations of an eating disorder to seek out information about the disorder and always believe that there is a way back to a healthier state of being. 10% True Self strength means that one's inborn desire to help others (altruism) is still intact and strong. One's caring and compassion for others is dulled, but not entirely gone. At 10%, the eating disorder part of the mind is strong, but not so strong that the remaining area of healthier thinking is completely conquered. Here and there, someone with a 10% True Self mindset can still hear the pleas from those who care about them, and believe that parts of what they are hearing about how ill they are appearing to others is true and not a manipulation. Someone with only 10% remaining of who they originally thought themselves to be is someone who can absolutely fight and win over the strength of an eating disorder.

Let's use another simple illustration to conquer the confusion and false sense of hopelessness brought on by eating disorder thinking by looking at Illustration No. 4. On the left hand side of the upward slope, the starting point is noted (10% True Self). On the far right hand side of the downward slope, the ultimate goal, or 99% True Self can be seen. At the peak of both slopes is the halfway point, also known as the 50/50 mark. There are incremental marks going up and down each slope to denote progress in the journey toward regaining True Self territory.

Family, friends, treatment providers and victims of actual eating disorders all need to share the same picture in their minds of the progress and process of recovery toward regaining at least 99% of the True Self mindset in order for this method to work properly. Those who have other ways of understanding and working toward healing are not incorrect or wrong, but as has been stated in earlier chapters, choosing *one single, unified vision that is shared among all those involved in the healing process* will go a long way toward achieving the actual goal of regaining all of the necessary strength for the benefit of the True Self thought process.

An eating disorder is, after all, a thought process that involves utilizing confusion from inside and outside the victim to maintain and increase mental and physical damage. This confusion needs to be countered by having everyone involved behave 'as if' they are willing and able to use one single method and way of thinking about healing. The largest part of the solution to the problem of eating disorders is, once again, to remove the confusion that this thought disorder feeds upon.

There are a few things to know about this process of healing from an eating disorder that will provide everyone involved in the effort with a sense of hope going forward. These few pieces of information about the process of healing also allow for a greater chance that those involved with helping as well as the one actually suffering with the eating disorder mindset can track their own progress.

Tracking progress provides an incremental, small, daily means of knowing just how much territory the sufferer has been able to take back. It lets everyone know at the same time what is going on inside the secret thoughts of someone who has an eating disorder. It allies those who wish to be helpful with the one who wishes to be helped. It reduces misunderstandings about just what the definition of true progress is. These small but important few pieces of information untwist the mirage and lies of the eating disorder thought process and help everybody involved make sense out of something that otherwise would never make any sense.

The thought process of an eating disorder is powerful enough, at 90% strength to use the thoughts of others, the negative input from media and upbringing, to validate itself. Let's look at the first piece of important information about healing from an eating disorder to straighten out the misunderstandings promoted by the mindset of an eating disorder so that the team of helpful people in the life of someone with an eating disorder can share a common way of thinking.

As you can see in Illustration No. 4, the left hand side of the slope from 10% True Self strength leading up to the 50/50 mark is an uphill slope. This is because going from a small amount of True Self strength to the halfway point has a different meaning than the one commonly held by most people: As you regain True Self territory from 10% to 50%, the journey feels more difficult.

Most people commonly hold the belief that as you make progress toward healing from an eating disorder, the journey gets better or easier. But the eating disorder mindset has twisted everything backward so that just the opposite is true. The journey grows more difficult, up to a certain point (the 50/50 mark) and this is a truth about healing from eating disorders that the entire treatment team and the victim must realize in order not to be tricked along the way.

If the eating disorder mindset that lives inside the victim and outside in those who care about him or her can prevail, the belief that the process of healing gets better as you go forward will only cause the victim to live in despair as they sense that just the opposite will actually occur. This is why eating disorder treatment often does not result in long term success in terms of healing. The sufferer becomes weary of making attempts at healing, and the number of treatment failures only serves to validate the hopelessness of the effort. But understanding that as a victim of an e/d makes progress toward regaining territory they will feel *worse instead of better* up to the halfway mark lets everybody involved in the healing process know that good progress is being made when the victim feels increasing distress and little or no progress is being made when they feel comfortable.

Feeling comfortable while working on healing from an eating disorder in the early stages of the process actually translates into not making progress toward healing, if one understands the twisted logic of the eating disorder correctly. Accepting this concept means understanding that the logic of the eating disordered thought process is actually the reverse of reality.

On the left hand side of the slope, i.e., making progress from 10% True Self strength to the 50/50 mark, there are certain milestones along the way that can be seen to help orient both the victim and those who are involved in the healing effort. Because an eating disorder operates much the same way in anyone who has the disorder, the same thoughts and actions can be seen. Fighting fire with fire means that we can use this 'traceability' of the eating disorder thought process to know exactly where a person is in their healing process from 10% to 50%. We can use the rigidity of the way an e/d works inside the mind of the victim in order to understand how to conquer it.

During the first few days in a structured inpatient or residential treatment program, it is common for a newly admitted patient to try everything in their power to get out of having to stay within the confines of that structure. Whether someone comes to inpatient hospital or residential treatment of their own choice or because of the leverage of an intervention or health consequences, nearly everyone in the first week or so of their treatment experience wants to 'undo' their choice to continue it. This is because the eating disorder mindset resists the very structured environment that challenges its strength and has the ability to separate its twisted, backward logic from the healthy normal common sense which belongs to one's True Self.

With few exceptions, if the treatment environment appears to lack enough structure so as to distress one's eating disorder, the common reaction by the newly admitted patient is a state of pleasant cooperation. Remember that when one has an eating disorder mindset, most everything one perceives is reversed. It is true at this point of healing as well. Wanting to get out of treatment is generally a sign that the treatment is sufficiently threatening to the eating disorder and therefore a good treatment. Wanting to stay inside of the treatment experience is generally a sign that the treatment environment is too low of a structure to be threatening to the e/d and therefore a poor treatment choice.

Parents, significant others and friends would all be well-advised to note that any calls to "rescue" the newly admitted patient from a distressing treatment environment is merely a sign that they need ample encouragement to stay the course and take the treatment one day at a time. Any person who truly cares about someone who needs to heal from an eating disorder is doing the ultimate disservice to the healing process by heeding whatever the newly admitted patient is saying and helping them to leave treatment.

There are other signs that treatment has the potential to be effective, even while such signs are unpleasant to deal with. After the first week of inpatient hospital or residential treatment, when it is clear that nobody is going to help the newly admitted patient to 'escape' the realities and discomforts of their new environment, the eating disorder thought process begins a second form of attack on its victim. This is so that the victim will choose to either leave treatment or find a way to 'trick the treatment system' to keep the eating disorder at its current or greater percentage of strength.

An eating disorder 'attacks back' at any forward progress the victim makes in regaining True Self territory. Each and every time forward progress is made, the thought process of an e/d is threatened, and to regain its former, stronger position, it attacks back. It does this in two separate and distinct ways while one is in a highly structured environment such as an inpatient hospital or residential program: first by working against the physical comfort of the sufferer, and next, by attacking the psychological and emotional comfort of the sufferer.

Once a victim of an eating disorder has settled into the structure of an inpatient or residential program, having discovered that there is nobody on the treatment team or in the circle of outside helpers who misunderstands the nature of the eating disorder, nobody who will enable the eating disorder to regain strength by helping the person to leave treatment, the next phase of healing can begin. This is where bonding with one's treatment team and peers comes into play, so that the first mode of attack by the eating disorder can be traversed and left in the past.

The eating disorder, if it could speak, would say something like "I do not like it that you have surrounded yourself with people who make it difficult for me to maintain my control over your bodily functions. Therefore, I am going to step up my attacks against your body so that you give into me and allow me to get back or keep the strength that I had prior to your coming into treatment."

Of course, an eating disorder does not literally 'speak' out loud to its victim, but instead sends messages such as these loudly enough within the mind of the e/d sufferer so that they can nearly be 'heard'. Those who are attempting to help someone with an eating disorder need to be able to know the 'voice' of an eating disorder even though at this stage it remains mostly secret in the private thoughts of the individual who is plagued with the disorder.

This private, internal 'voice' of the eating disorder is actually the person's own voice, which they silently 'hear' as part of their own thoughts. In the beginning stages of healing during proper inpatient or residential treatment, there is no identifiable separation between the part of the mind that contains the twisted eating disorder thoughts and the other, weaker, part of the mind that contains healthy, normal, common sense thoughts which we call the True Self. It all feels jumbled up into one single 'voice'.

Later we will see how successful progress toward healing gets these two voices separated so that the sufferer who has an eating disorder can turn these two parts against one another and continue past the 50/50 mark to get relief and make progress toward regaining 99% True Self power.

To return to the discussion about the first stages of healing from an eating disorder, the thought process finds itself trapped in a high structure, attempts to escape the structure, and failing an escape, turns to fighting its victim with increased attacks against their physical body. It does this in the hopes of regaining power. The victim needs to bond with staff and peers within the treatment program in order to tolerate physical discomfort. Fortunately, physical discomfort that results from approximately two to three weeks of continuous abstinence from eating disorder actions then dissipates, leaving the victim relieved of physical attacks and knowledgeable as to how their own mind and body are deeply connected.

Some, but not all of the possible physical attacks that are common to the beginning two to three weeks of inpatient or residential treatment that are brought on by a trapped eating disorder are bloating, stomach cramps, frequent urges to bring up food (also known as regurgitation), acid reflux, water retention, headaches, restless leg syndrome, nightmares, sleep disturbance, restlessness, anger, frustration, agitation, tearfulness, heart palpitation, racing thoughts, obsessions, increased urges to harm oneself (such as thoughts that one should cut, bang, hit or pummel oneself), suicidal thoughts and isolative behavior. These are not all of the physical manifestations of an attacking eating disorder, but these are some of the most common at this stage in the process of healing.

During this stage, the eating disorder thought process is still a secret, needing to be kept by the sufferer. Those who care about the victim of an e/d usually have no idea about what the private thoughts of a sufferer are. Any time the negative physical urges are avoided by someone at this phase of healing, the fear is that the negative 'voice', or messages will grow so strong that too much tension, also known as anxiety, will be felt.

When too much anxiety is felt by someone attempting to resist their eating disorder, they only know how to control and reduce the anxiety (which often feels but is not life-threatening) by taking an eating disorder action.

As has been mentioned before, true healing from an eating disorder thought process only occurs when one obtains continuous, consecutive days of abstinence from eating disorder actions. This is not easy for a person suffering with an eating disorder to achieve. As they gain day after day of abstinence (or negative action-avoidance), the voice or negative thoughts of the e/d becomes louder and stronger. This is why a highly structured program offered by a residential or inpatient hospital treatment environment is necessary. Outpatient therapy is not generally a sufficiently strong enough structure with which to cordon-off eating disorder messages or actions.

As soon as someone with the e/d thought process leaves the therapist, psychiatrist, nutritionist or outpatient group, they are plagued with an increasingly stronger set of negative thoughts that must be acted upon since there is nothing beyond the outpatient experience to attempt to stop the behavior.

Any e/d behavior is sufficiently soothing enough to promote an avoidance of healing and validate that healing is futile. Outpatient therapy with an eating disorder thought process that is more than 51% stronger than one's True Self, then, generally does not provide a permanent solution to weaken and place an eating disorder in remission.

Most families and victims of eating disorders prefer outpatient treatment, however, because they often misunderstand just how strong the e/d thought process really is. They also prefer outpatient because it provides a way to perform the actions of healing on the outside even if it does not result on true healing on the inside. As long as the sufferer can continue working at their job, attending school, staying within the minimal bounds of parenting and in general appearing to be 'normal', they can avoid severe feelings of shame and embarrassment. Admitting oneself to treatment is usually the most resisted and last thing a sufferer will allow themselves to do for this last reason alone. Unfortunately, there are many treatment providers who also do not understand that left improperly treated, an eating disorder is chronic, progressive over time and ultimately fatal. Seeing someone who is suffering from a strong eating disorder thought process in outpatient therapy, then, inadvertently contributes to the progression of the disorder.

The therapist who agrees to this usually becomes part of the enabling process, part of growing the disorder ever-stronger over time rather than effectively impacting and putting the disorder in permanent remission.

Knowledgeable therapists can do much to eliminate themselves from the long list of enabling providers of care. Accepting e/d patients with a clear goal of preparing them to admit to inpatient hospital or residential treatment and drawing a very clear transition date to a higher level of care is an effective way to utilize outpatient therapy so that it is helpful rather than harmful to a victim of a strong eating disorder.

Meeting with an entire group of caring individuals who are emotionally, financially, legally and otherwise connected to the sufferer of an eating disorder, laying out what an eating disorder is and how to effectively work toward realistic treatment outcomes is definitely in order for the therapist who specializes in eating disorder treatment. Helping the group of caring individuals behave in a loving yet effective way toward someone who has an eating disorder while preparing everyone involved for the inpatient treatment and later, aftercare experience is an important part of the overall healing process. Being the sole provider of treatment on an outpatient basis for the victim of a strong e/d, unfortunately, is not appropriate and only promotes a short-term façade of assistance.

The next phase of healing from an eating disorder, which involves making progress toward the 50/50 mark against psychological and emotional 'push-backs' from the eating disorder thought process will be described in a following chapter.

Process of Recovery

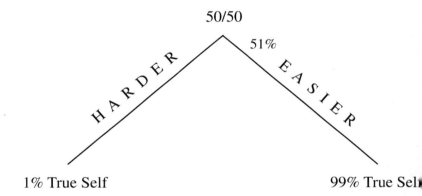

Chapter 9

IN CHAPTER 8, PHASE I, we covered tracing of the progress of recovery from an eating disorder by setting out how the e/d uses a 'reverse logic' to attempt to trick a new patient, their family and treatment team to reduce the structure from residential or inpatient down to outpatient care so the eating disorder is able to maintain its former strength.

We went over how a caring team of individuals can untwist the reverse logic of an eating disorder to figure out if residential or inpatient treatment is sufficiently effective to fight the eating disorder. We uncovered the nature of the eating disorder just enough to discover that in the first half of residential or inpatient treatment, the eating disorder 'attacks back' at any forward progress the victim is able to make in terms of obtaining sequential days of continuous abstinence from e/d behaviors.

The first part of the attack by the eating disorder to discourage all involved from making true, lasting progress in getting back True Self territory is a physically-oriented attack against the victim's physical comfort level. The greater the physical discomfort, the more forward progress in treatment the victim is actually making. We discussed how common it is for people who do not have an eating disorder to mistake forward progress (i.e., physical discomfort in the early stage of treatment) as treatment failure when it is, in fact, the surest sign of initial treatment success.

We also learned that outpatient treatment is not generally, by itself, an appropriate way to obtain permanent, lasting healing from an eating disorder. Outpatient treatment is a good way to prepare a victim and his or her family and supporters for entrance into inpatient or residential treatment, but by itself, is not sufficiently structured or strong enough to contain and stop e/d behaviors long enough to create an effective healing outcome.

We discussed why outpatient usually *seems* like it is a good choice when in fact, in reality, it is just the opposite wherever eating disorders that are stronger than 51% in strength are concerned.

We went over these areas with regard to healing from an eating disorder in order to change misunderstanding into understanding, and remove the ability of the eating disorder to use our own healthy, normal common sense toward its own negative goals. Instead, now we can use our own healthy, normal common sense toward decoding the reverse logic of the eating disorder to promote forward progress toward healing from an eating disorder.

Having achieved a basic understanding about the first phase of tracing the path of healing, let's move on to the second phase of tracing forward progress toward healing from an eating disorder. The second phase involves the eating disorder fading in its strength with regard to attacks upon a victim's physical comfort and a short-lived but progressive increase with regard to attacks upon a victim's psychological and emotional comfort.

Recall that an eating disorder, as a thought process, utilizes its own 'negative voice' within the mind of someone who suffers from the disorder to slowly but surely take over 'True Self' territory from its victim. As it slowly encroaches over the True Self, healthy, normal common sense thinking is replaced with increasingly rigid, stuck, resistant and non-sensical logic.

Those around a victim who is slowly losing healthy, normal, common sense thinking become alarmed when they attempt to assert their own healthy, normal, common sense logical statements over those of the sufferer. Such assertions are often met with a variety of interesting methods of resistance. One form of resistance that appears in response to pleas by family and friends to have a healthier relationship with food results in illogical arguments by the victim. Another form of resistance looks like agreement and compliance, and can go as far as sounding like genuine gratitude for the concerned person's attempt to care. Another form of resistance is for the victim to create a façade, or false appearance of cooperation in order to distract and soothe concerned people around them so that the eating disorder behavior and thoughts can be carried out without interruption by real, effective help.

False help in the form of attendance at individual therapy sessions, fake help by trips to health spas (which can actually serve to grow an eating disorder quickly), the outward appearance of weight gain with frequent demonstrations of weigh-ins (the victim usually finding ways to add water or other temporary weight to increase the viewable weight measurement) and other methods are all commonly used by a victim of an eating disorder. The reason victims of eating disorders expend so much energy to

protect their eating disorder mindsets is because if they do not do so, they are in a great
deal of psychological and emotional distress.

Psychological and emotional distress is
often felt physically in the body of the eating
disorder victim as tension, and known otherwise as anxiety. When an eating disorder is
misdiagnosed as an anxiety disorder (usually
because the victim hides any e/d symptoms
when seeing a physician), it is unfortunate but
rather common for anti-anxiety medication to
be prescribed. By itself, without proper residential or inpatient structured treatment that
accompanies psychological care by a trained
therapist, anti-anxiety medication treats only
the physical outcome or symptom of an eating
disorder but does absolutely nothing to change
the growing strength of e/d thoughts. Because
of the addictive nature of some anti-anxiety
prescription medications, a second problem is
often added and intertwined closely with the
first problem of the eating disorder, making effective healing even more difficult since both
problems now need to be resolved.

The eating disorder utilizes anxiety as its
primary 'driver' of the need to take negative actions against a victim. Mild anxiety is felt as a
"warning" by the victim originating from his or
her eating disorder thoughts that if he or she
doesn't 'behave' according to the negative messages to take negative actions, a greater level

of anxiety will be felt until the victim 'gives in' to the e/d voice. Only when an e/d victim 'caves' or 'gives in' to the ever stronger negative voice with its twisted messages regarding bingeing, purging, compulsive exercising, laxative use, metabolic enhancers, food restriction, obsessive-compulsive thoughts and behaviors, drinking, drugs, promiscuous acts, shopping, stealing, etc., does the anxiety become temporarily relieved. Unfortunately, each acting out of the urge to perform a negative action based upon the e/d warning of greater anxiety results in a stronger eating disorder thought process and a weaker True Self.

Because it is rare that the e/d thought process can be acted upon by a victim as many times as the e/d would want its victim to, a victim usually must find one or more methods to 'quiet down' the eating disorder negative voice. This often results in cross-addiction. Cross-addiction is most commonly seen in some of the above examples of behaviors, but when done repeatedly, becomes in and of itself addictive and super-entwined with the eating disorder. A common thought error by those who care about people with eating disorders is that any drug, alcohol or other addictive behavior needs to be seen as the first or primary problem. An eating disorder can stay hidden for many extra and unnecessary years while it creates greater damage due to this common error or confusion.

In order to heal from an eating disorder, the victim must be clear enough from drug and alcohol use (this includes over and under-the-counter drugs, and also means so-called recreational drugs to include marijuana) to participate in eating disorder treatment. It is true that an eating disorder victim needs to detox and receive addiction treatment as the first treatment undertaken, but usually the error in thinking that this is all that is needed requires many addiction treatments and later, more serious hospitalization for eating disorder treatment. The best way to think about how to treat an eating disorder when other substances or behaviors are also present is that the eating disorder sits underneath everything else that is negatively impacting a victim, and must be treated in order to remove a great deal of pressure from the victim to utilize negative substances or behaviors. Therefore, good addiction treatment should be successfully completed, immediately followed by good eating disorder treatment without a break in between one treatment and the next.

While the eating disorder, when there is one, is usually always 'primary' or first, addiction treatment must come before eating disorder treatment so that a clear mind is available to participate in the eating disorder treatment. It is not a good idea, then, to obtain addiction treatment for a victim of an eating disorder followed

by outpatient eating disorder treatment. While
the victim may become 'treatment weary', it is
very important to take care of both chemical
dependency and eating disorder issues in the
right order. If this is not done (and of this writing, unfortunately, this is not done frequently),
relapse back to chemical dependence (or other
addictions) and ever stronger and more harmful eating disorder behaviors are the common
result. When considering treatment options, it
is less expensive and more effective to do this
process "right" the first time, rather than have
to do it half-way (meaning, listening to and following the victim's way of treating his or her
own e/d) and have to undergo primary treatment an average of five times.

So psychological and emotional distress is
most commonly felt as anxiety, and once eating disorder treatment has begun, and once the
first phase of treatment has passed, this is the
largest part of the feeling state of someone who
has entered Phase II of inpatient or residential
treatment for their eating disorder.

As the victim moves into Phase II, their body
no longer exhibits most or all of the physical
discomfort that was felt during Phase I. Those
who care about someone receiving residential
or inpatient treatment can be fooled at this
stage by the victim's eating disorder because
it appears that once the physical symptoms of
discomfort have been removed, the entire eat-

ing disorder has been removed. This is simply not so, and is, in fact, yet another 'trick' by the eating disorder thought process to regain strength over its victim.

The physical discomfort once felt by someone in effective treatment does fade, however, untwisting the logic of the eating disorder involves understanding that a new, greater discomfort is about to be utilized by the eating disorder. The effective form of residential or inpatient treatment is still working, and should be left in place during Phase II, without interruption, no matter how strongly the e/d victim pleads with outside supports for removal from treatment.

At about 20% True Self strength, the eating disorder thought process shifts from attacks against the body to attacks against the mind. This attack process involves increasingly disturbing thoughts within the mind of the sufferer of the eating disorder patient. These increasing negative thoughts grow 'louder' at certain times and quiet down at other times, depending upon the form the eating disorder took when it was unchecked, prior to effective treatment.

For example, suppose the victim of an e/d primarily used compulsive exercise as a means to keep the eating disorder 'voice' quieted down prior to entering effective residential or inpatient treatment. After Phase I has been successfully completed, Phase II begins, and the e/d 'voice' grows very frightening and ever-louder every time exercise is either discouraged or limited as part of a good e/d program.

Another example of how the e/d voice becomes louder, causing increasing psychological and emotional discomfort with each successive day of abstinence from e/d behavior is when a person in effective treatment used to answer the negative voice prior to treatment by restricting or ritualizing their food behaviors. Once in Phase II of eating disorder treatment, a structured, individualized meal plan is to be followed and the eating disordered negative voice grows ever louder when healthy eating habits are promoted by a patient who is attempting to follow their meal plan.

In fact, any small amount of steady structure imposed by following a residential or inpatient treatment program for healing from an eating disorder outrages the eating disorder thought process. It responds to this form of structure by torturing its victim with increasing amounts of anxiety that, at its peak, cause the victim to want to stop the treatment process at any cost and regardless of any obvious near or future consequence to themselves or others.

The anxiety can become so strong, the negative thoughts discussed in an earlier chapter so loud, that victims feel as if they are 'crawling out of their skin' and often describe the feeling of anxiety as 'killing' or 'life-threatening'.

This negative thought process works with increasing strength during the entire second phase of eating disorder inpatient or residential treatment, which is why in the last chapter all parties involved with an e/d victim were fore-warned not to assist in enabling the victim to leave treatment due to increasing distress or discomfort. The same warning is offered here: The surest sign that eating disorder treatment is effective in shrinking the e/d mindset (doing much toward the healing goal of putting the e/d in remission) is that the psychological and emotional discomfort of the e/d patient is seem-ingly becoming stronger, not weaker.

In a discussion about the third phase of treatment, we will go over the passing through of this distress to a state of incredible relief, and a reversal of the loudness and frequency of the negative eating disorder thought process. Often, knowing that there is an absolute end to the most distressful phases of healing from an eating disorder is enough to help all those who care about someone who has an eating disorder tough out the hardest parts.

Phases I and II of effective eating disorder treatment, then, are indeed the hardest part of the entire healing process. Sometimes only a realistic, truthful vision of exactly what to expect is enough to carry both the victim and his or her entire treatment team through the thirty to sixty days of both phases to the 50/50 mark, where much-needed relief from crushing anxiety first beings to be experienced by all involved.

Chapter 10

IN CHAPTER 9, PHASE II, we covered tracing of the progress of recovery from an eating disorder by noting that after the physical attack by an e/d has subsided, the next phase of healing involves a great deal of emotional and psychological discomfort. The final phase of good eating disorder treatment is still highly structured, and involves attaining and holding onto all of the progress that has been made.

Phase I takes about two to three weeks to move through. Phase II generally takes about thirty to forty-five days, and the remaining time in a highly structured eating disorder treatment environment can take up to an additional thirty days when done properly. This would appear to be an incredibly long period of time, considering that customary drug and alcohol addiction treatment at the inpatient level is often from 21 to 30 days.

However, drug and alcohol treatment is considerably different in requirement and content than eating disorder treatment and the challenges that the e/d patient must face are often substantially different than that faced by the chemically dependent patient. There are similarities between drug and alcohol vs. eating disorder intervention and treatment, but greater familiarity with the truth about eating disorders reveals more differences than similarities. Eating disorder treatment should be considerably longer than drug/alcohol treatment for a variety of reasons too numerous to address here, but in understanding what is involved in each of the three phases of e/d treatment, the most important points supporting longer stays at higher levels of care will be more easily understood.

Let us turn now to understanding key points related to an eating disorder patient's involvement in the third phase of treatment. Understanding what is involved in Phase III will help those who care about a victim of an eating disorder avoid the all too common mistakes that unfortunately often contribute to treatment failure and later relapse.

First and most important is the need to understand that since an eating disorder is a thought process which has been resident for many more years than it has been visibly obvious, it is 'dug-in' to the patient's psyche and has become a part of *who* the patient thinks they are. Moreover, anything that has been in place consistently for a long period of time, and an eating disorder certainly qualifies in this regard, reaches a state of its own balance, also known as 'homeostasis'.

Although we do not want this twisted balance existing in someone we care about, there it absolutely is, and needs to be respected for the power that it has to ruin the victim's life and downgrade the lives of others who are in any way attached to them. An eating disorder seeks to maintain this dark balance or homeostasis within its victim, and the pull to reverse any forward progress made in the first three weeks of treatment pales to the amount of pull to reverse any forward movement made in the following thirty to 45 days. In other words, until the 50/50 mark has been achieved and held in place for a considerable amount of time, the pull to relapse at 49% is felt by a victim as being *stronger* to return to the eating disorder thoughts and behaviors.

However, something positive begins to happen at about the 45% mark during good, thorough eating disorder treatment: Here and there, the eating disorder 'voice' begins to weaken and at times, drop off. This dropping off process is noticed by the patient almost as if it is an accident. Quite suddenly, after a half day or two days of being entirely without any eating disordered negative thoughts, it occurs to the patient that something does not feel right, or that something odd is missing. It is difficult for them to identify just what this missing thing is, but there is a strange feeling of relief associated with it. The newly relieved patient usually thinks that they must be doing something 'bad' or wrong to have this empty space feeling within them.

What is typically happening at about the 45% mark is that the eating disorder victim is feeling their very first moments of True Self strength, as well as a small window into the reality of what life will be like without their eating disorder. Careful attention will need to be paid to this 'missing thing' by treatment staff so that the e/d patient can make up their own mind as to whether they like the new feeling or not. Of course they like the feeling, but it is important that nobody like the new feeling more than they do, for the accomplishment of shrinking the eating disorder voice belongs only to the person who had the ability to fight it in the first place: the patient themself.

Prior to reaching the first small windows of relief, it is typical for an eating disorder patient in Phase III to feel incredibly fatigued. Fatigue is the hallmark of hard work in the fight against the eating disorder. Loss of sleep, eating disorder nightmares, flare-ups of eating disordered thoughts regarding the victim's body image (always inaccurate but felt as very accurate), irritableness with regard to small details, comparisons made between other patients and oneself and large demonstrations of authority-figure disputes are all typical signs that Phase III of structured eating disorder treatment is effective.

Treatment staff, family, outside treatment providers and friends all need to understand the positive signs so that they can continue to support the patient in continuing to stay the course of treatment no matter how difficult it feels. All involved need to repeatedly remind the e/d patient that the treatment experience not only becomes *harder* up to a point, it also comes with a promise of a soon-to-be-felt 'dropping off' of the worst and strongest messages sent by the victim's eating disorder. Repeated promises that relief is on the way need to be made, for while a patient is in Phase III, the eating disorder homeostasis is being broken, challenged and pushed back, perhaps for good. Of course the e/d seeks to regain its former strength by utilizing the five senses (seeing, hearing, smelling, tasting and touching) of the victim to twist any outside evidence of progress. This is, in effect, how the eating disorder uses psychological and emotional attacks to regain its former position of strength over the victim's True Self.

At this stage, those who have great support for holding their ground, forward movement up the left-hand side of the process of recovery slope by adherence to the strict structure of good e/d treatment, and a terrific sense of altruistic vision and 'buy-in' to the promise of what a life in recovery from an eating disorder might feel like will succeed. Until a patient can experience the first hints of eating disorder thought 'drop off' and solidify for themselves the fact behind their own success, others outside of the patient must hold the hope and strength for them and never, ever be fooled by the e/d thought process.

It is too easy, however, for those outside of the victim's treatment environment to be fooled, for phone calls and visits to someone in Phase III can easily be misunderstood. For example, hearing how tired or fatigued a patient is can inspire a parent or other family member to think that the staff is unrelenting, lacking in compassion or not able to identify what the special needs of the patient are. Yet incredible fatigue in an eating disorder patient who is in Phase III of their treatment experience is the surest sign of impending victory there is.

Victims are fatigued because their total internal psychological and physical experience has been effective in fighting against the awesome strength of the eating disorder. It is not easy to hold one's ground against what feels like an impending anxiety attack, but patients in Phase III actually rally against anxiety attacks and learn to not only get through them, but think about them differently. This takes a considerable amount of energy and contributes to psychic fatigue.

In Phase III, the appetite may or may not return to a victim of an eating disorder, but either way the e/d thought process takes hold of either state of mind and uses it against the victim to attempt a return of its strength. Functional eating with or without an appetite results in a great deal of fatigue. Fatigue is only one of many signs that Phase III is being successfully traversed. There are so many other milestones and markers with which to see that e/d treatment is working. The treatment team that includes inside staff and outside family, friends and treatment providers needs to agree to remain positive in the face of what only appears to be negative (but is actually positive in reality) challenges to further forward movement by the eating disorder patient.

A patient complaining of being 'triggered' by other patients who are more active in their eating disorder behaviors is one who is also making good progress in Phase III of e/d treatment. This is not the time to believe the negative mind

of the patient, but instead is the time for the cohesive inside and outside team to join together
and reassuringly explain that the 'triggering'
itself is a great sign of progress toward the
50/50 mark.

A patient complaining that their old clothes
no longer fit is going through a neurological
shift from malnourishment to nourishment.
The senses of sight and touch are impacted by
the slowly renourished brain, but the meaning of these changes is still bonded to the
eating disorder sense of meaning. The patient
feels their own skin against their own familiar clothing and interprets (incorrectly) that
treatment *is not* working because clothing feels
much tighter than it once did. The fact that the
patient is experiencing any increasing sense-
oriented change in sight or touch at all is the
surest sign that their brain is healing from the
malnourishment of disordered eating.

Informed staff and outside team members
are well advised to repeatedly state how positive
this change is, and how the further continuation of forward progress will later be thought of
differently. The skewing of the eating disordered
thought process should be pointed out as well
as the need for continued True Self strength to
be developed to change this perception-lie created by the victim's eating disorder.

A small amount can be said here about
body image problems, although body image

problems and issues are vast and require much more study than can be offered in this book. In Phase III of structured residential or inpatient treatment, it is a sure sign that the treatment is effective if body image issues actually worsen or increase instead of decrease. Later, after the 50/50 mark has been reached, body image issues will still be a problem for most victims of eating disorders, even from 50% to 99%, since of all the eating disordered problems resident in the thoughts of the victim, body image issues are often the last problem to fade.

The reason that body image issues appear to worsen or increase in Phase III of eating disordered treatment is because the balance of the changes from eating disorder thought process to True Self thought process is shifting, which creates a sense of confusion. A person's entire paradigm or total identity has only been experienced through the lens of the twisted, negative eating disorder for a very long time. Therefore, any shift or change that is sensed by the victim is still interpreted as "bad" at the internal level.

An e/d patient in Phase III checks the mirror and body parts, clothing sizes and other inaccurate measurement devices more frequently during this phase because of the need for outside validation that the e/d is still strong enough for them not to feel 'lost', or without the felt-sense of control through use of the eating disorder mindset.

Families and other outside supports for the victim of an eating disorder need to understand that increased remarks about how the patient is feeling increasingly "fat", "out of shape", etc., while in treatment is a sure sign that the treatment is actually working. In other words, patients who are practicing active eating disorder behavior do not need to check on how their bodies are doing very often for they know with certainty that by restricting, compulsive exercising, vomiting and drug taking (in any combination or all of the above), the e/d voice will stay quieted and they will be psychologically and emotionally more comfortable with themselves.

A patient in Phase III will begin to feel increased anxiety or internal tension as they heal within their own minds because they are not practicing their eating disordered behavior while in treatment, thus throwing them into psychological and emotional distress. Families, staff and others should applaud this sign and encourage the patient in Phase III of treatment to continue doing a good job in further distressing their eating disorder.

With this type of support, Phase III eventually ends and the 50/50 mark is reached. For most, Phase III does not end abruptly, but appears to 'drop off' in terms of eating disordered negative messages and physical urges to return to the sense of control felt when eating disordered behaviors are utilized. For a few, the eating disordered thoughts suddenly appear to 'give up' and go away for increasing lengths of time, signaling the attainment of the 50/50 or halfway mark of recovery. For most, however, there is a moving forward and moving back process that is sensed and experienced by the e/d victim while in the final days of treatment. This is not unusual, and is actually yet another sure sign that progress is being made.

By the time the final two to three weeks of residential or inpatient treatment have been experienced, it is normal for an eating disorder patient to feel alternatively happy, then sad, up then down, terrified and anxious, then relieved and relaxed. As long as nobody inside and outside the treatment environment can be fooled into removing the patient from the structured environment, Phase III will in fact pass and the 50/50 mark will be achieved.

The next treatment hurdle will be to hold onto the halfway mark progress point, and create a thorough, gradual and effective step-down in structure as part of the aftercare program. We will cover this in the next chapter.

Chapter 11

IN CHAPTER 10, PHASE III, we covered tracing the progress of recovery from an eating disorder by noting just some of the signs that the halfway, or 50/50 mark has been reached. We went over not only how one reaches such a point, but how one can hold onto the territory they have regained for use by the True Self. We discussed how family and treatment providers can avoid being fooled by the eating disorder thought process into giving back any of the hard-won territory by making innocent and unknowing errors utilizing healthy normal common sense. Instead, we further revealed the twisted thought process of the eating disorder so that once decoded, an eating disorder patient can be properly supported in continued recovery.

Just prior to discharge from a residential or inpatient eating disorder program, the eating disorder itself makes one final attempt from a place of strength to wrench its victim back onto the left-hand side of the process of recovery slope. (See Illustration No. 4) This, for lack of any more simple way to describe it, is called *the teeter-totter effect.*

The teeter-totter effect occurs when an e/d patient is just about ready to discharge from primary, highly structured treatment to an aftercare or outpatient program. The teeter-totter effect is where there is vacillation between the 45% to 50% mark in e/d recovery, and the 51% to 55% mark in e/d recovery.

Understanding how an eating disorder utilizes 'rocking' back and forth between moments, hours or days (even weeks) of periods of e/d weakness to moments, hours or days (and even weeks) of e/d strength can make the difference between the e/d patient being supported properly or being fooled into thinking they are failing in their ability to hold onto their 51% True Self territory.

Perfectionism is one of the symptoms and hallmarks of the eating disorder thought process. The eating disorder utilizes perfectionism within family members and the patient to set up a set of criteria or expectations. A patient who has reached the 50% to 51% of strength needed in order to move onto the aftercare phase is understandably proud of this accomplishment. Their family, friends and outside treatment provider network are also hopeful and understandably excited by this positive state of events.

However, the eating disorder mindset is rather sneaky, and can utilize the happiness and sense of accomplishment of all concerned to support overconfidence and perfectionistic expectations of continued forward progress. This expectation, held by anyone involved, from patient to treatment team and family, is risky and unadvisable. This is so because the eating disorder thought process ebbs and flows, or comes and goes in its strength and ability to negatively impact its victim.

Someone who has done the exhaustive, difficult work of putting their eating disorder into a weakened state (i.e., 51%) will find it terribly depressing and frustrating to admit to anyone that they are having a 45% experience for any temporary period of time. This will feel like a failure to them. Any family and friends noting that their loved one is still struggling with their body, mind and spirit when only the week before had seemed apparently free of the negative voice and all that accompanied it can be tricked into thinking of the backward movement in territory as a failure. The patient will not want to admit to the temporary difficulty they are experiencing for a variety of reasons that, at the time they occur, may seem quite logical.

The e/d patient teeter-tottering back and forth between 45% and 55% is tempted to mistakenly keep their backward percentage state to themselves so as not to worry or further trouble those who are supporting them in treatment. Often they feel guilty utilizing exceptions and resources and only wish to "get on with their life" to avoid guilt, shame and embarrassment by drawing out the healing process any longer than they think they can tolerate. The family and friends of an e/d patient, too, can be tricked by this teeter-totter effect and validate the eating disorder thought process further by simply asking, "what went wrong", or by some innocently stated comment that translates into shame and blame either to the patient or to the treatment staff.

None of this has to occur if all concerned come to understand that an eating disorder which is waning in its strength, moving toward a state of remission will naturally, as a positive process of healing, rise and fall in its level of strength for upwards of an additional thirty days after the halfway mark has been achieved. If all concerned understand that fluctuations in True Self territory and e/d strength are the norm rather than the exception as regards the process of recovery, then accurate expectations will lead to further forward progress without shame or blame adding to the difficulty of forward movement by the soon to discharge patient.

Further, any perfectionism held by family, friends and outside treatment providers can be utilized to strengthen the True Self efforts of the fledging patient rather than help the patient think about setting up a façade of well-being or strength to please those outside of the structured inpatient or residential treatment environment.

Having said this, we can move on to briefly describe an adequate aftercare plan for someone who has undergone thorough eating disorder residential or inpatient treatment. This chapter will in no way prescribe exactly what each individual's care should be, but will instead describe a somewhat new way to view what aftercare generally looks like when it is respectful of the power of an eating disorder to create relapse in its victim.

Aftercare should have a 'step-down' process. That is, every month or so following discharge from a highly structured residential or inpatient eating disorder recovery program, a person healing from an eating disorder should incrementally increase their involvement in real-life stressors and activities. This process of gradually stepping down in structure and gradually increasing real-life stressors and activities should continue without interruption from the first day of discharge from highly structured treatment through and beyond the end of the person's first year of recovery.

Graduated step-downs in structure prevent shame and embarrassment from re-entry into the mindset of someone who has passed the 51% recovery mark. Because the strength of the eating disorder thought process comes and goes with regard to its hourly and day to day strength level, often small slips in forward progress (noted by an increase in the strength of the negative, e/d voice not e/d actions or relapse) occur.

At the onset of increased e/d thoughts, the person undergoing a graduated step-down program of aftercare should 'step-up' their recovery related program activities and decrease non-recovery related real-life stressors for a period of ten to thirty days. Incremental step-down and step-up helps to prevent a feeling of hopelessness that may set in when the eating disorder thought process is temporarily on the rise.

The eating disorder thought process does not recognize the difference between good stressors (such as family gatherings, holidays, impending college testing, etc.) and bad stressors (such as rejection, grief, loss of employment, etc.). It only recognizes stressors as catalysts or sustenance for a regaining of its former strength within the mind of its victim. Everyday life brings with

it an experience of daily good and bad stressors, but adjusting well by utilizing one's True
Self perceptions and actions is largely due to
a gradual exposure of stressors instead of a
quick and overwhelming exposure.

Given the graduated step-down method,
it is wise to have a next lower level of care at
the ready for the newly discharged inpatient or
residential patient. At best, remaining within
the physical boundaries of 24 hour structure
without most of the individual and group peer
support of a structured full time program can
be the first step-down in a long series of transi-
tions to every day life. Next in the lower level of
care would be discharge from a continuation
program to a living environment that includes
some level of physical accountability for abstinence from eating disorder actions, combined
with a thorough outpatient program.

Some combinations of outpatient programs
for the continued support of eating disorder
recovery include individual therapy, individual
nutritional consultations, personal training
for structured exercise, individual psychiatric
consultations and ongoing group interaction
with the focus on recovery from eating disorders. Any trauma, grief or other issues that
were present at the time of intake to a highly
structured program may now be more safely
dealt with as part of the step-down outpatient
program. 12-step OA (Overeater's Anonymous)

program support is a desirable and long-term continuing support resource once formal treatment has concluded.

The person recovering from the 51% mark forward who utilizes a gradual step-down approach to their continued aftercare program can expect to have good days and difficult days, but has the right to expect to reach the 85% to 99% recovery mark from their eating disorder as a result of this slow, gradual approach to e/d healing within the first year of their recovery.

The remainder of the healing experience from the first year of recovery and beyond will be varied and experienced differently from one person to the next. Issues that contributed to the negativity of the eating disorder thought process will still be issues that need to be successfully dealt with as time passes. However, any issues that were formerly used as external validation for internal worthlessness will be largely removed as support for regrowth of the e/d mindset and its strength. It will perhaps be felt as a blessing that issues needing further attention will merely be just that, rather than the fuel for relapse, as long as a thorough, continued, graduated step-down process of recovery is utilized within the first year and beyond.

Chapter 12

LATE IN THE YEAR 2000, visionary owners and directors of chemical dependency and other related forms of treatment decided to answer a growing need for effective residential treatment for adult women with eating disorders. They envisioned a women's residential program that was not as highly structured as an inpatient medical facility, but just structured enough at the residential level so that women who did not qualify or require such a high level of medical inpatient hospitalization could utilize a slightly lower structure within which to heal from their eating disorders.

This is when and why The Victorian Program was developed, as an affiliated part of total residential treatment for those afflicted with addictions. Since that time, nobody could have predicted the miracles that have resulted from this original vision for women's residential eating disorder treatment. It is time to share some of the principles of the No-Resistance Method of treatment that is utilized at The Victorian House eating disorder with you now. These principles are based on a set of assumptions, some presented here, that contribute to the wonderful success stories that our former patients have experienced as part of this program.

Having learned what an eating disorder is and is not, and having gathered more information about how the healing process works, you now have a unique understanding about eating disorders that many people do not have. The education that you have received by reading this book will help you to appreciate the results that the Victorian House residential program has been able to provide the women who have gone through this program.

Some of the approximately 150 women who have come through the Victorian House program over the past five years have arrived after struggling with their eating disorders for most of their lives. We have successfully treated women, aged 18 and over, for anorexia, bulimia, compulsive overeating as well as those who have cross-addicted to drugs, kleptomania, co-dependence and alcoholism (and more) in addition to their eating disorders. They have come from all over the globe to reside for no less than sixty continuous days at the Victorian House residence. Often, after their primary care stay at Victorian House, our patients move on to enjoy an incremental step-down in structure over time, in thirty day increments, at our continuing care residential program called The Lido House.

Some of the women have arrived at Victorian House after having been through nearly every major and well-known eating disorder treatment facility in the United States. Others have been through one or two outpatient programs followed by an unsuccessful inpatient stay. Others have never been treated at a residential or inpatient level and admit for treatment for their very first time to the Victorian House. Regardless of their prior history of treatment, the requirements for admission to the Victorian House are relatively few, and all who are admitted have equal opportunity to make their Victorian House program, regardless of what had occurred before, their last formal structured program. This is because we utilize the No-Resistance Method of treatment at Victorian and Lido programs, and the results we have been able to achieve are relatively phenomenal in comparison to these women's prior treatment experiences. It is not too bold to add that results from The Victorian Program are remarkable when compared to the general statistics with regard to successful eating disorder treatment outcome. We acknowledge that beyond the fact that eating disorders are the most fatal of all formal DSM-IV disorders, the current statistics for successful remission from active eating disorder behavior are quite grim. The Victorian Program is increasingly successful in confronting and creating good treatment outcomes. This is primarily due to the use of a unique new method of approaching treatment called 'The No-Resistance Method of Treatment' for eating disorders. Buried in its title is the philosophy of the entirety of the method in just two words: No Resistance.

The No-Resistance Method of treatment involves a few assumptions about structured care that contributes to the effective outcome we see from those successfully completing the Victorian and Lido programs. First, we assume that patients and their families must become experts, in their own right and in their own way, in understanding and coping with the general subject of eating disorders. It is not enough to have medical, psychological and trained certified staff carry the knowledge about what eating disorders are and how to properly place an eating disorder in remission. The nature of an eating disorder itself dictates that *the person within whom the eating disorder resides must absolutely understand and fight their own eating disorder.* Therefore, at Victorian House, we assume that our role is not to place ourselves on an omnipotent pedestal with our patients and their loved ones, but instead take a supportive and relational role.

In this regard, families and loved ones attached to someone with an eating disorder are involved in an intimate way during the course of treatment once a woman is admitted to the Victorian House program. In many programs, it is customary to separate the woman from her outside support system and only include the immediate family in a structured family program one time during the end phase of treatment. At Victorian House, the No-Resistance Method dictates that those closest to the identified patient have been a part of the eating disordered system, continue to be a part of that system and, if not evolved into part of the actual the treatment team, will not be a positive support once the woman leaves structured care. So another assumption is made in utilizing the No-Resistance Method for treating eating disorders: *Those closest to someone with an eating disorder need to become an integral part of the team allied with the True Self in order for the woman to succeed in her fight against her eating disorder.*

In everyday terms, this means that once a woman has settled into the Victorian's residential program, having made her own decision as to whether or not she will "drive" her own True Self resistance against the side of her mind that carries the eating disordered thoughts, she will need an increasingly knowledgeable and supportive outside team waiting for her once she leaves the experience of more highly structured care. To do otherwise sets a newly discharged person up for relapse, since innocent and unwitting 'un-doing' of what has been learned while in structured care will automatically occur once the woman reintegrates back into her former lifestyle. Family, friends and significant others need to understand exactly the same information, method and ways that they can be helpful in allying themselves with the person's emerging True Self in order to avoid becoming utilized by the person's eating disorder. The eating disorder will utilize anyone who maintains ignorance or a separate stance from the complete residential treatment and family/friend/significant other team as a so-called "back door", or means to regain twisted thinking territory and therefore cause a former patient to relapse.

Each person intimately involved in the healing process must adopt, on an 'as-if-we-all-agree' basis, the same exact understanding and action in order for the eating disordered part of the mind to continue moving from the 50/50 mark downward toward the 99% True Self goal. When there are no primary enablers, when there is only outside validation for internal positive growth, the eating disorder mindset continues to move into a state of permanent remission. Each forward movement from the 50/50 mark to an increasing percentage point shows individual members of an outside caring team just how well they are doing to maintain their status as allies with the True Self. The fight against the eating disordered thought process is healing to anyone involved, and more often than not, entire families begin to heal from the negative effects of eating disordered thinking that has been hidden in the minds of family members and spouses, often for many generations.

One of the nicest side-effects of effective treatment that we see at Victorian House is that when a woman has been successful in attacking her own eating disordered thinking, she automatically and without fully meaning to inspires others who are plagued in her family and private life to heal from this harmful thought process as well. It is very common for one or more family members to have active eating disorders, and even more common for one or more family members to have inactive eating disordered thoughts. However, when someone turns their healthy, normal True Self thinking and behavior against the twisted and harmful eating disordered thinking, healing is seen not only in the patient but also, seemingly by osmosis, in the rest of the family.

The No-Resistance Method utilized by the staff at Victorian House provides a way for the staff to avoid professional burn-out that is such a common outcome for providers who specialize in working with those suffering with eating disorders. Because staff members are encouraged to remove themselves as the point of main resistance to a woman's eating disorder, the woman only has her own eating disorder to resist instead of someone who is attempting to help them. The staff at the Victorian House are trained, often for months in advance of their formal employment, in the same education and methods as the patients themselves will utilize during the course of their treatment, and everyone...staff, family and patients, utilize one common language with which to make the invisible eating disorder visible, and therefore conquerable.

With eating disorders, the thought process up to the halfway point of healing is "cookie-cutter", but still the individual circumstances of the woman must be taken into account in order to achieve the treatment goal. This is done by way of taking a detailed history and assessment and focusing strongly on the goals that are important as part of the healing outcome for the woman admitting to treatment. In other words, another assumption of the No-Resistance Method is: *In order for a woman to willingly turn her True Self against her eating disorder, she has to strongly anticipate, believe in and desire the results of treatment.* Translated into action, this means that a woman entering the Victorian House who would otherwise avoid treatment because it would interrupt her attempt to complete college should be helped to actually attend college as part of her continuing treatment. A woman who wishes to become independent of her family system (economically as well as emotionally and psychologically) should be helped to find employment and a suitable living environment of her own once more highly structured residential program has been successfully completed.

In an earlier chapter, the subject of altruism was briefly reviewed. Built into the Victorian House program is an intimate understanding of the built-in traits that women with eating disorders tend to have. Their need for control, negativity and perfectionism is strong and has been utilized for a long time by the eating disorder part of their minds. Another positive trait, called altruism, is also built-in to the character makeup of women who suffer from active eating disorders. The No-Resistance Method of Treatment makes another assumption in order to gain effective outcomes in healing from eating disorders: *The same traits that an eating disorder usurps within its victim to cause harm are the same traits that can be utilized by one's True Self to help heal him or her.*

Therefore, at Victorian House, The No-Resistance Method is utilized to promote a woman first understanding what these traits are and next taking dominion over them to add strength and force to her True Self fight against her own eating disorder. In other words, a woman who used to utilize extreme control via practicing her eating disorder will now gradually learn how to utilize control to weaken her eating disorder. Individualized treatment plans at Victorian House include daily assignments tailored strictly to the individual's needs *at that moment* to help her understand and, at first, behave 'as-if' she has the ability to control her reactions. By practice utilizing staff and peers, she repeats these as-if assignments until they result in the woman feeling her own mastery over her decision making process. When she actually likes the significantly different outcome that her strengthened True Self feels, these 'as-if' decisions and behaviors become part of a new system of behavior that is habitual and nearly automatic. Only highly structured programs can corral eating disorder behaviors and thoughts enough to utilize them against themselves in these *on-demand* interventions.

Further, The No-Resistance Method requires that the staff act as one cohesive team. Very often in multi-disciplinary inpatient treatment, a variety of staff is utilized, but each staff member brings with them their own understanding and method of providing care for their shared patients. The eating disorder mindset lives within this well-meant yet scattered philosophical and theoretical attempt to heal, often un-doing even the best attempts at effective treatment. This Method requires staff to be ever-ready with their cell phones and walkie-talkies to 'team up' on a moment's notice regarding individual challenges on a moment to moment basis, often 24 hours a day. The eating disorder within the patient utilizes the status quo of staff leaving their shifts and more staff coming onto their new shifts to build splits between staff communications and actions to assist the eating disorder in keeping or increasing its strength.

Instead, at Victorian House, all staff members speak to any and all staff members at any time to obtain a cohesive mindset well before providing assistance or direction to a patient. The eating disorder within the patient is flustered by this, the True Self bolstered, and the woman learns quickly to utilize her skills of negotiation, manipulation, intellect and coping to fight her own eating disorder rather than attempting to turn staff members against one another and thus lose such strong support. A woman is even more successful when she learns how to utilize such strong staff support by translating it outward to parents, friends and significant others. In effect then, everybody involved becomes a member of a cohesive treatment team regardless of the role played in the world of the eating disorder patient. Nobody can then be utilized as an ally by the eating disorder, and the usual struggles between outside treatment providers, outside family, friends and loved ones are simply not seen as part of The Victorian House program.

At the outset of care, a patient signs a complete and full release so that family, outside treatment providers and inside staff can all freely communicate without limitations about the patient's eating disorder, leaving nobody who is involved in the healing process in the dark. Patients who ally with their eating disorders and attempt to rescind their releases may legally do so, but also understand prior to formal admittance that they must expect to exercise this legal right at a referred program, not at Victorian House. First and foremost, our ethical goal is to be *effective* providers of treatment, and to have our ability to do this removed or limited then ethically requires us to make a competent referral to a higher level of care. We see this as a criterion of acuity since a woman who is given informed consent about how The Victorian House program works prior to intake and who then rescinds her release is far too ill with her eating disorder to be appropriate for a residential level of care and requires referral to a higher level of care. By the time most women who suffer from active eating disorders come to the Victorian House, they clearly understand that they may not have the ability to undergo further treatment experiences due to financial, legal, social, professional or health consequences. Most are willing to cooperate with this understanding since it reflects only the highest goals toward effective outcomes in treatment by the staff. Women who expect to put their eating disorders in remission as a result of participating in The Victorian House program expect and accept full disclosure of their progress in treatment as part of the healing process. Their acceptance of this as fact is also one of the earliest predictors of successful outcome, and indicates that they will be a good 'match' for the type of program we offer.

Women who admit to the Victorian and Lido programs do not have the type of medical problems that would require admittance to a licensed hospital facility. This means that while there may be health consequences that have resulted from long time practice of an eating disorder, no emergency medical care is required on a moment to moment basis during the course of residential treatment at Victorian House. We provide on site nursing assistance and medical and psychiatric intervention where needed by appointment, but we also offer outside practitioner care by patient choice.

The No-Resistance Method of eating disorder treatment can then be utilized further because of this lack of morbid acuity (where ongoing medical intervention is not required) in a variety of ways. One of the best ways that the The No-Resistance Method can be seen in every day action with women who are in The Victorian House program is before, during and after meals and snacks.

After our nutritionist (who is a registered dietician familiar with working with those who have eating disorders) begins meeting with Victorian patients on a weekly consultation basis and a careful, detailed treatment plan and goal is set forth, the nutritionist then creates and updates a weekly, individualized meal plan. Our patients utilize their own individualized meal plan to prepare and eat their meals from. It is usual and customary for nearly all patients to feel fearful of this process, so they are brought gently and gradually to the point of developing a healthy relationship with food. The No-Resistance Method is utilized carefully here so that the woman has a sense of control over just how much fear and anxiety she must face at every meal and snack she is assigned to plan, prepare and consume throughout each treatment program day. You will see staff carefully observing minute behaviors that individual patients are having during their struggle with food and deliberately not immediately confronting these behaviors. This is remarkably different in the realm of treatment, where

BARBARA COLE

there is generally a tendency to over-supervise and intervene or under-supervise and refrain from intervention during the course of eating disorder nutrition.

Staff is trained to a high level of personal impulse control, so that they increase their observations that they may share difficulties with food with all other staff and come up with a cohesive, across-the-team approach to intervening and assisting in a non-resistant way with a patient. Most interventions are done in private, mostly individually with the woman's case manager, therapist and nutritionist. Any intervention with food that is done in front of other patients is usually extremely passive and is given from a "back-seat" position to the woman's own position. In other words, the assumption is made in utilizing The No-Resistance Method that: *Staff supports a woman's fight to heal her relationship with food by positioning support from behind, not from pushing or pulling from a position in front of where the patient is at.* The woman herself leads this symbolic 'dance' since it is a dance with excessive fear and anxiety that she must negotiate, and she herself will push as far as she can when at least 1% of her True Self is voluntarily resident in our treatment program.

We at Victorian House understand that we are, individually, not powerful enough to fight any person's eating disorder. By the time we en-

THE EATING DISORDER SOLUTION

counter an active eating disorder, it has nearly completely overtaken the woman's mind and has proven its awesome strength to us. However, with one leader proposing strategies and an entire staff (to include family and others outside The Victorian House) carrying these therapeutic strategies out, the powerful eating disorder is literally and figuratively "surrounded" by True Self allies. This sense of incredible support placed in the hands of the woman considering losing her own eating disorder is often enough to create the miracle of recovery, seen time and time again in the healthy, happy, liberated faces of those who long ago were our patients.

For further information about The No-Resistance Method of Eating Disorder Treatment, please review a copy of the soon to be published book titled, *The No-Resistance Method for Treatment of Eating Disorders – For Practitioners as well as The No-Resistance Method of Eating Disorder Intervention* (Publication expected in 2006, Trafford Publishing/Winter Publishing, by Dr. Barbara Cole).

Chapter 13

CONCLUSION: NEXT STEPS TOWARD THE EATING
DISORDER SOLUTION

THIS BOOK IS BY NO means conclusive or all-encompassing in its simple overview of the No-Resistance Method of healing from eating disorders. The next steps in healing from an eating disorder are multi-faceted and involve quite a bit of energy, but are positive, possible and hopeful.

For practitioners, further training in The No-Resistance Method of Eating Disorder Treatment and Intervention is becoming available by way of workshops, conferences, seminars and additional publications. *The No-Resistance Method of Treatment for Eating Disorders – Practitioner's Guide* will be published in 2006-2007. *The No-Resistance Method of Eating Disorder Intervention* (both by Trafford Publishers/Winter Publishing) will be available in the near future as well. The Victorian House Programs located in Newport Beach, California, can provide hands-on training for qualified certified and licensed personnel where position openings permit. For information about any of the above, please visit websites at: drbarbara-cole.com or eatingdisordertreatment.com or contact the Victorian House Programs directly at (800) 647-0042.

For family, friends, and significant others of someone who has an eating disorder, follow-up action to reading this book should consist of getting advice from knowledgeable professionals experienced in working with those suffering with eating disorders. To find such professionals, you may wish to begin your search by contacting the International Association of Eating Disorder Professionals (www.iaedp.com) at (800) 800-8126 or The American Association for Marriage and Family Therapy (www.aamft. org) at (703) 838-9808. There are literally thousands of websites and referral services available to you as of this writing.

For the man or woman suffering from an eating disorder, the next positive step in the direction of beginning your journey toward healing after reading this book should be to visit your medical doctor. Be specific and rigorously honest about all of the symptoms you have experienced and are now experiencing as a result of your eating disorder so that your physician can rule out any physical consequences that your eating disorder may have already caused you. Next, consult a mental health practitioner who specializes in eating disorder treatment to plot a course of healing for yourself. Visiting the above websites or calling the numbers listed above will be a good way to begin the research that should lead to taking quick, decisive actions to confront and work against your eating disorder. Remember that vast numbers of people have absolutely healed from eating disorders and you can, too. Refuse to listen to the negative voice in your own mind when it tells you that your symptoms aren't as bad as someone else's, that you don't deserve to thrive and live well, that nobody cares about you. The eating disorder thought process is the complete reverse of what is actually true. Stick with the advice of people around you who seem to irritate or frighten your eating disorder thoughts. Try handing over decision-making to someone you trust so that your eating disorder will not attack you quite as much for speaking up against it. Tell others what is really going on, and then let others help you. People who suffer with eating disorders are often unable to gain enough strength over their eating disordered thoughts to reach out for real help all by themselves. Remember that inadequate or too little help is the same as no help at all. Go for the most help that you can despite what your negative mind is saying to you about it. Let yourself take a break from your normal activities in life. Take a "time-out" for effective treatment so that afterward, you can enjoy all the gifts that are a part of living a life entirely without an eating disorder. You deserve this and much, much more. You are worth it!

Bibliography

Ansbacher, Heinz L., and Ansbacher, Rowena R., *The Individual Psychology of Alfred Adler*, New York: Harper & Row, Publishers, Inc., 1956

Ansbacher, Heinz L., and Ansbacher, Rowena R., *Superiority and Social Interest*, New York: W. W. Norton & Company, Inc., 1979

Bell, Rudolph, *Holy Anorexia*, Chicago: The University of Chicago Press, 1987

Bloom, Carol., Gitter, Andrea, et al., *Eating Problems*, A Feminist Psychoanalytic Treatment Model, New York: Basic Books, 1994

Bruch, M.D., Hilde, *The Golden Cage,* The Enigma of Anorexia Nervosa, Massachusetts: Harvard University Press, 1978

Brumberg, Joan Jacobs, *Fasting Girls*, The History of Anorexia Nervosa, Massachusetts: Harvard University Press, 1988

Bynum, Carolyn Walker, *Holy Feast and Holy Fast*, The Religious Significance of Food to Medieval Women, California: The Regents of the University of California, 1987

Bynum, Carolyn Walker, *The Resurrection of the Body in Western Christianity*, 200-1336, New York: Columbia University Press, 1995

Claude-Pierre, Peggy, *The Secret Language of Eating Disorders*, New York: Random House, 1997

Cordell, Franklin D., Ph.D., and Giebler, Gale R., Ph.D., *Psychological War on Fat*, Illinois: Argus Communications, 1997

Costin, Carolyn, M.A., M.ED., MFCC., *The Eating Disorder Sourcebook*, A Comprehensive Guide to the Causes, Treatments, and Prevention of Eating Disorders, Illinois: Lowell House, 1996

Garner, David M., and Garfinkel, Paul E., Eds., *Handbook of Treatment for*

Eating Disorders, 2nd Edition, New York: The Guilford Press, 1997

Hall, Lindsey, and Ostroff, Monika, *Anorexia Nervosa,* A Guide To Recovery, California: Gürze Books, 1999

Hendricks, Jennifer, *Slim To None*, A Journey Through The Wasteland of Anorexia Treatment, Chicago: Contemporary Books, 2003

Hollis, Judi, Ph.D., *Fat Is A Family Affair,* A Guide for People with Eating Disorders and Those Who Love Them, Minnesota: Hazelden Information & Educational Services, 1985

Johnston, Anita, Ph.D., *Eating in the Light of the Moon*, How Women Can Transform Their Relationships With Food Through Myths, Metaphors & Storytelling, California: 2000

Kabatznick, Ronna, Ph.D., *The Zen of Eating*, Ancient Answers to Modern Weight Problems, New York: 1998

Levenkron, Steven, *The Best Little Girl in the World,* New York: 1978

Piaget, Jean, *The Construction of Reality in the Child*, New York: 1971

Sacker, Ira M., M.D., and Zimmer, Marc A., Ph.D., *Dying To Be Thin*, Understanding and Defeating Anorexia Nervosa and Bulimia – A Practical, Lifesaving Guide, New York: 1987

Schaefer, Jenni with Rutledge, Thom, *Life Without Ed*, How One Woman Declared Independence from Her Eating Disorder and How You Can Too, New York: McGraw-Hill

White, Michael, and Epston, David, *Narrative Means to Therapeutic Ends*, New York: W.W. Norton & Company, 1990

Biographical Information: Dr. Barbara Cole

Dr. Barbara Cole is the Clinical Director of the Victorian House of Newport Beach, California, where she has developed a unique method of residential treatment for women with eating disorders. Her publications include *The Eating Disorder* Solution (Trafford Publishing/Winter Publishing), *The No-Resistance Method of Treatment for Eating Disorders – Practitioner's Guide*, (Trafford Publishing/Winter Publishing – Pending), Gifts *of Sobriety* (Hazelden Publishing and Information), The No-Resistance Method of Eating Disorder Intervention (Winter Publishing - Pending), *Don't Tell a Soul* (Rosen Publishing), *Alex The Great* (Rosen Publishing), *Color and You,* (Revelli, Inc.) and more. She has been in private practice as a marriage and family therapist in Newport Beach, Corona del Mar and Los Angeles, California for many years, and adds to a wealth of experience her years as a clinician at The Betty Ford Center and prior to that the Program Director of many licensed treatment facilities in northern California. Dr. Cole has a bachelor's degree in World & Comparative Literature, a master's degree in Creative Writing and English, a second master's degree in Clinical Psychology, and doctorate degrees in Psychology and Metaphysics, as well as hypnotherapy certification and licensure. She is a clinical member of the American Association of Marriage & Family Therapy as well as a member of the International Association of Eating Disorder Professionals. She has dedicated her life to making unnecessary human suffering optional.

You may contact Dr. Cole or learn more via her website at www.drbarbaracole.com.

ISBN 141207593-9

9 781412 075930